NEED to KNOW

HIGHER PHYSICS

Paul Chambers
Douglas Gavin

HODDER
GIBSON
AN HACHETTE UK COMPANY

Photo credits: p61 top, Phil Degginger/Alamy; p61 bottom, Universal Images Group North America LLC/Alamy; p64, Fotolia

Orders: please contact Bookpoint Ltd, 130 Park Drive, Milton Park, Abingdon, Oxon OX14 4SE. Telephone: (44) 01235 827827. Fax: (44) 01235 400454. Email: education@ bookpoint.co.uk. Lines are open from 9 a.m. to 5 p.m., Monday to Saturday, with a 24-hour message answering service. Visit our website at www. hoddereducation. co.uk. Hodder Gibson can also be contacted directly at hoddergibson@ hodder.co.uk.

First published in 2019 by
Hodder Gibson, an imprint of Hodder Education
An Hachette UK Company
211 St Vincent Street
Glasgow, G2 5QY

Impression number 5 4 3 2 1

Year 2023 2022 2021 2020 2019

Typeset by Aptara, Inc., India
Printed in Spain

A catalogue record for this title is available from the British Library.

ISBN: 978 1 5104 5119 3

Hachette UK's policy is to use papers that are natural, renewable and recyclable products and made from wood grown in well-managed forests and other controlled sources. The logging and manufacturing processes are expected to conform to the environmental regulations of the country of origin.

MIX
Paper from
responsible sources
FSC™ C104740

Contents

1 Our dynamic universe 5

  1.1 Motion: equations and graphs 5

  1.2 Forces, energy and power 11

  1.3 Collisions, explosions and impulse 16

  1.4 Gravitation 21

  1.5 Special relativity 24

  1.6 The expanding universe 27

  End of section 1 questions 32

2 Particles and waves 34

  2.1 Forces on charged particles 34

  2.2 The Standard Model 39

  2.3 Nuclear reactions 44

  2.4 Inverse square law 47

  2.5 Wave–particle duality 50

  2.6 Interference 53

  2.7 Spectra 58

  2.8 Refraction of light 62

  End of section 2 questions 66

3 Electricity 68

  3.1 Monitoring and measuring AC 68

  3.2 Current, p.d., power and resistance 71

  3.3 Electrical sources and internal resistance 76

  3.4 Capacitors 80

  3.5 Semiconductors and p–n junctions 86

  End of section 3 questions 90

4 The assignment 92

Getting the most from this book

This *Need to Know* guide is designed to help you throughout your course as a companion to your learning and a revision aid in the months or weeks leading up to the final exams.

The following features in each section will help you get the most from the book.

You need to know

Each topic begins with a list summarising what you 'need to know' in this topic for the exam.

Exam tips

Key knowledge you need to demonstrate in the exam, tips on exam technique, common misconceptions to avoid and important things to remember.

Key terms

Definitions of highlighted terms in the text to make sure you know the essential terminology for your subject.

Do you know?

Questions at the end of each topic to test you on some of its key points. Check your answers here: hoddereducation.co.uk/needtoknow/answers

Synoptic links

Reminders of how knowledge and skills from different topics in your Higher course relate to one another.

End of section questions

Questions at the end of each main section of the book to test your knowledge of the specification area covered. Check your answers here: hoddereducation.co.uk/needtoknow/answers

1 Our dynamic universe

1.1 Motion: equations and graphs

You need to know

- how to use the equations of motion for objects moving in a straight line with constant acceleration
- how to draw and interpret velocity–time, displacement–time and acceleration–time graphs
- how to draw and interpret motion graphs for objects with a constant acceleration – for example, a ball thrown vertically upwards and a bouncing ball
- how to describe an experiment to measure the acceleration of an object down a slope
- how to calculate the rectangular components of a velocity

Equations of motion

You should already know these equations for an object moving in a straight line with constant acceleration:

$$\text{average speed} = \frac{\text{distance}}{\text{time}} \quad \text{or} \quad \bar{v} = \frac{d}{t}$$

$$\text{average velocity} = \frac{\text{displacement}}{\text{time}} \quad \text{or} \quad \bar{v} = \frac{s}{t}$$

$$\text{acceleration} = \frac{(\text{final velocity} - \text{initial velocity})}{\text{time}} \quad \text{or} \quad a = \frac{v - u}{t}$$

The equation above can be rearranged to give:

$$v = u + at$$

where v is the **final velocity** of the object, u is the **initial velocity**, a is the **acceleration**, s is the **displacement** and t is the time taken.

Exam tip

Be careful when doing calculations with equations involving vector quantities such as velocity. Vectors have direction. The objects in questions may be moving in a straight line, but you still need to consider their direction. Make one direction positive and then any motion in the opposite direction is negative.

Key terms

Final velocity The velocity at the end of the part of motion being analysed.

Initial velocity The velocity at the start of the part of motion being analysed.

Acceleration The rate of change of velocity – how much the velocity of an object changes in one second.

Displacement The distance travelled in a particular direction.

The displacement of an object can be found from:

$$s = ut + \frac{1}{2}at^2$$

These two equations can be combined to give a third equation:

$$v^2 = u^2 + 2as$$

There is also a final relationship that can be useful:

$$s = \frac{1}{2}(u + v)t$$

Exam tip

Note that there are five variables in these equations but that each equation contains only four of them. If you know three of the variables, you can use a combination of the equations to work out the other two.

Graphs of motion

You should already know how to draw and recognise velocity–time graphs for an object moving at a **constant velocity**, an object moving with a **constant acceleration** and an object moving with a constant **deceleration**.

Now look at how to draw the acceleration–time and displacement–time graphs for these three types of motion.

Key terms

Constant velocity If an object is moving at a constant velocity, its velocity is not changing. Velocity is a vector quantity, so the object must be travelling in a straight line with a constant speed.

Constant acceleration This is when the velocity of an object changes by the same amount each second.

Deceleration This is a negative acceleration, usually when an object is slowing down. However, it can also mean an acceleration in the opposite direction.

Constant velocity

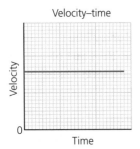
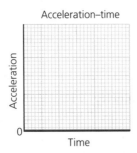
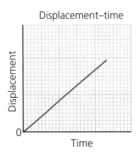

Figure 1.1 The graphs of motion for an object moving with constant velocity

■ The **gradient** of the velocity–time graph is zero, so the acceleration is zero.

Exam tip

Remember that the gradient of a velocity–time graph gives the acceleration of an object and that the area under a velocity–time graph gives the displacement of the object.

Key term

Gradient The slope of a line.

- If you are analysing a graph that has a straight line, you can find the gradient, m, using:

$$m = \frac{y_2 - y_1}{x_2 - x_1}$$

- The area under the velocity–time graph increases by the same amount each second, so the displacement–time graph is a straight line through the origin.

Constant acceleration

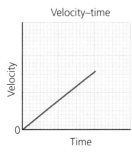
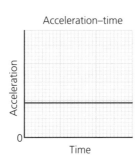
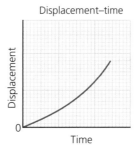

Figure 1.2 The graphs of motion for an object moving with a constant positive acceleration

- The gradient of the velocity–time graph has a constant positive value, so the line on the acceleration–time graph is parallel to the time axis; acceleration has a constant positive value.
- The area under the velocity–time graph increases by an increasing amount each second, so the line on the displacement–time graph is a curve of increasing positive gradient.

Constant deceleration

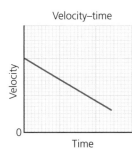
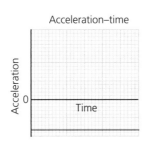
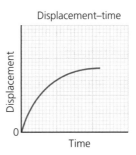

Figure 1.3 The graphs of motion for an object moving with a constant negative acceleration

- The gradient of the velocity–time graph has a constant negative value, so the line on the acceleration–time graph is parallel to the time axis but below that axis; acceleration has a constant negative value.
- The area under the velocity–time graph decreases each second, so the line on the displacement–time graph is a curve of decreasing positive gradient.

Graphs of an object accelerating due to gravity

There are two velocity–time graphs you need to know about that describe an object being accelerated due to gravity. The first graph is for an object thrown straight up which then falls vertically downwards, as shown in Figure 1.4.

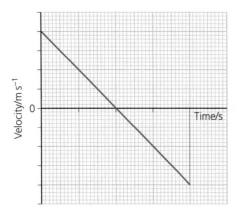

Figure 1.4 The velocity–time graph for an object thrown vertically upwards and then caught

- In this graph, motion upwards is positive.
- The ball starts off with a positive velocity because it is thrown upwards.
- As the ball rises, its positive velocity decreases until the ball reaches its maximum height where its velocity is zero.
- The ball then starts to fall. As it falls, its speed increases but it is now travelling downwards so its velocity is negative.
- The gradient of the line is the ball's acceleration. The gradient is negative and constant because the ball is always accelerating downwards towards the centre of the Earth at the same rate – the opposite direction in which it was thrown.

The second graph you need to know about is for a bouncing ball, as shown in Figure 1.5.

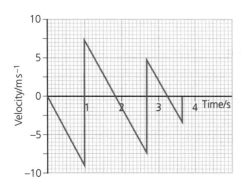

Figure 1.5 The velocity–time graph for a bouncing object

Need to know Higher physics

- Again, in this graph motion upwards is positive.
- The ball is dropped and starts to fall. As it travels downwards, its velocity is negative.
- The ball then hits the ground and rebounds. It is now travelling upwards, so its velocity is positive.
- When the ball's velocity reaches zero, it is at its maximum height.
- The ball then starts to fall again, so its velocity is negative.
- It then hits the ground and the process is repeated. Each time the ball bounces, its rebound height becomes less and less until it eventually reaches zero.
- As before, the gradient of the line is the ball's acceleration. The gradient of each section is the same and this is a constant negative value because the ball is always accelerating downwards at the same rate.

Measuring the acceleration of an object down a slope

In the Higher physics course you need to be able to describe a series of experiments. One of these is how to measure the acceleration of an object moving down a slope.

The apparatus shown in Figure 1.6 can be used for this experiment.

Exam tip

This is not the only method for doing this experiment. In the exam you could be asked about a different experimental set-up. It is important that you understand the principles behind doing this experiment.

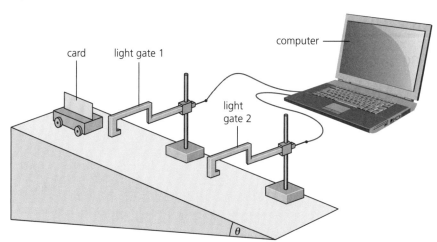

Figure 1.6 Measuring the acceleration of an object down a slope

- Two light gates are connected to a computer, which acts as a timer.
- The computer times how long it takes for the piece of card to pass through light gate 1 (t_1).
- It then times how long it takes the card to travel from light gate 1 to light gate 2 (t_2).

- Finally it times how long it takes for the card to pass through light gate 2 (t_3).
- The computer works out the initial velocity of the vehicle, u, at light gate 1 using:

$$u = \frac{\text{length of card}}{t_1}$$

- It then works out the final velocity, v, of the vehicle at light gate 2 using:

$$v = \frac{\text{length of card}}{t_3}$$

- The acceleration, a, can now be calculated using:

$$a = \frac{(v - u)}{t_2}$$

Rectangular components of a velocity

When analysing the velocity of an object travelling at an angle to the horizontal, it can be useful to split the velocity into **rectangular components** (vertical and horizontal).

Key term

Rectangular components Components of a vector at right angles to each other.

For example, a ball is projected at 30° to the horizontal at $15\,\text{m s}^{-1}$, as shown in Figure 1.7.

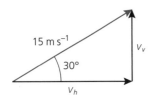

Figure 1.7

Using trigonometry you can work out the horizontal component, v_h, and the vertical component, v_v, of the velocity of the ball, v:

$$v_h = v \cos \theta = 15 \cos 30 = 13\,\text{m s}^{-1}$$

$$v_v = v \sin \theta = 15 \sin 30 = 7.5\,\text{m s}^{-1}$$

Do you know?

1 A car starts from rest. It accelerates at $0.25\,\text{m s}^{-2}$ for 12 s. Calculate the final velocity of the car.

2 A ball falls freely from rest for 0.24 s. Friction forces are negligible. What is the displacement of the ball?

3 A train travelling at $24\,\text{m s}^{-1}$ decelerates at $0.12\,\text{m s}^{-2}$. Calculate the speed of the train when it has travelled 384 m.

4 Figure 1.8 shows the acceleration–time graph for an object starting from rest.

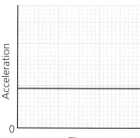

Time   **Figure 1.8**

Draw the corresponding velocity–time graph and the displacement–time graph.

5 Sketch the velocity–time graph for a bouncing ball dropped from a height. Your graph should show that the ball has bounced three times. Numerical values are not required on either axis.

6 A ball is projected at $22\,\text{m s}^{-1}$ at 30° above the horizontal. Determine the initial vertical component of the velocity of the ball.

1.2 Forces, energy and power

You need to know

- that force is a vector and how to use vector addition to solve force problems
- the difference between balanced and unbalanced forces
- the effects of Newton's first and second laws of motion
- how friction affects a moving object
- what is meant by terminal velocity
- how to draw free body diagrams
- how to resolve rectangular components of a force
- what is meant by the conservation of energy

Forces

- A force is either a push or a pull.
- A force can affect the motion of an object. It can change its speed, the direction in which the object is travelling or its shape.
- Forces are vectors. This means that they have a size, units and a direction.
- When forces are added together you must use vector addition techniques. If the forces are not aligned, this will require using either scale drawings or trigonometry.

Synoptic link

You need to be able to resolve vectors for velocities as well as forces. See page 10.

Balanced forces

- When the vector addition of all the forces acting on an object equals zero, this is the same as the object having no force acting on it. The forces are described as **balanced forces**.
- When the forces acting on an object are balanced, there is no change to its motion.
- This is described in **Newton's first law of motion**: If an object is at rest or moving in a straight line at a constant velocity, it will continue to do so unless acted on by an unbalanced force.
- In other words, if an object is stationary it will not start to move unless an unbalanced force acts on it.
- If an object is already moving, it will continue to travel in a straight line at the same speed unless an unbalanced force acts on it.

Figures 1.9 and 1.10 show two examples of balanced forces. In Figure 1.9 the forces on the boat are balanced – the weight downwards is balanced by the buoyancy force upwards. In Figure 1.10 the weight of the mass is balanced by the upwards force of the spring.

Key terms

Balanced forces When the vector sum of all the forces acting on an object equals zero. This is equivalent to no force acting on the object.

Newton's first law of motion If the forces acting on an object are balanced, the object will not accelerate.

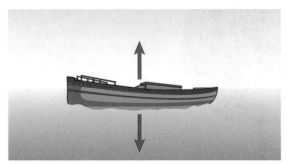

Figure 1.9

Figure 1.10

Unbalanced forces

- You can see from Newton's first law that when the forces acting on an object are balanced, the object does not accelerate.
- Therefore, when the forces acting on an object are **unbalanced forces** they will cause the object to accelerate.
- Remember that velocity is a vector, so if an object is moving at the same speed but is changing direction it is accelerating.
- The effect of unbalanced forces can be described by **Newton's second law of motion**. The equation for this law is:

$$F = ma$$

where F is the unbalanced force, m is the mass and a is the acceleration.

Key terms

Unbalanced forces Forces that cause an object to accelerate.

Newton's second law of motion This states that the acceleration of an object is proportional to the unbalanced force and inversely proportional to its mass.

Exam tip

Be careful with the equation for Newton's second law of motion. F represents the overall unbalanced force in the direction being considered, not any individual force given in the question. You may have to add individual forces and/or resolve a force before you can use this equation.

Synoptic links

- Unbalanced forces can also be used to explain the movement of charged particles in an electric field. See page 35.

- It is an unbalanced force that causes a projectile to follow a curved path. See page 22.

Example

A car accelerates from rest. It has a mass of 1250 kg and the engine produces a constant force of 880 N.

Its initial acceleration, a, is:

$$\frac{F}{m} = \frac{880}{1250} = 0.70 \, \text{m s}^{-2}$$

After 3 seconds, the frictional forces acting on the car are 410 N. At this point the resultant force driving the car is:

$$880 - 410 = 470 \, \text{N}$$

which gives an acceleration of:

$$a = \frac{F}{m} = \frac{470}{1250} = 0.38 \, \text{m s}^{-2}$$

Friction

- **Friction** is a force that always opposes the motion of an object.
- In other words friction always acts in the opposite direction to the direction in which the object is moving, as shown in Figure 1.11.

Key term

Friction A force that always opposes an object's motion.

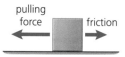

pulling force friction

Figure 1.11 The friction acts on the movement of the block to slow it down

- The faster an object moves, the larger the opposing friction force becomes. This is why objects such as cars have a maximum speed. This is called their **terminal velocity**.
- When an object falls from a large height, the frictional forces acting on it increase as it falls and accelerates.
- When the values of the frictional forces reach the same value as the object's weight, there is no longer an unbalanced force acting on the object and it falls with a constant velocity (see Figure 1.12). It has reached its terminal velocity.
- The terminal velocity of a falling object can be controlled by a parachute. When the parachute opens, it creates significantly more friction which causes the parachute and object to continue to fall with a lower terminal velocity, as shown in Figure 1.13.

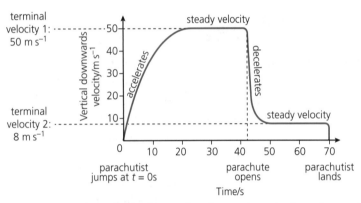

Figure 1.13 This graph shows the change in velocity after a sky diver's parachute is opened

Free body diagrams

- The forces acting on an object can be analysed using a free body diagram.
- For example, a box is dragged across a floor with a force of 25 N. The frictional forces acting on the box are 10 N.
- You can draw a free body diagram to find the unbalanced force.
- You can see from Figure 1.14 that the unbalanced force acting on the object is 15 N.

Rectangular components of a force

- Force is a vector and therefore has direction as well as its size.
- When a force is acting at an angle to a surface, it can be useful to resolve the force into **horizontal and vertical components** to the surface.

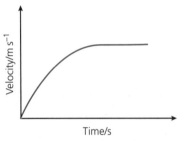

Figure 1.12 Graph to show the velocity of a falling object

Figure 1.14

- For example, a 65 N force is acting at 25° to a horizontal surface, as shown in Figure 1.15.
- You can resolve the force into horizontal and vertical components using trigonometry.
- The horizontal component is:

Figure 1.15

$$F \cos \theta = 65 \cos 25 = 59\,\text{N}$$

- The vertical component is:

$$F \sin \theta = 65 \sin 25 = 27\,\text{N}$$

- This can be useful if you are asked to describe the horizontal and/or vertical motion of an object.
- The component of a weight acting down a slope, F, is given by:

$$F = mg \sin \theta$$

where m is the mass of the object, g is the gravitational field strength and θ is the angle of the slope measured from the horizontal.

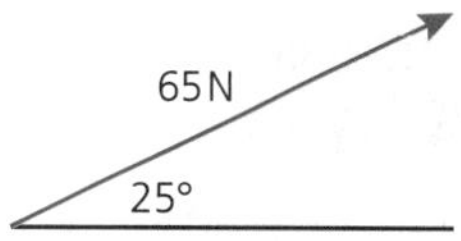

> ### Exam tip
>
> You need to remember this equation – it is not on the relationships sheet given to you in the exam.

Conservation of energy

- The law of conservation of energy states that energy cannot be created or destroyed, only changed from one form to another.
- You need to be able to use the following equations for gravitational potential energy, kinetic energy and work done:

$$E_p = mgh$$

$$E_k = \tfrac{1}{2}mv^2$$

$$E_w = Fd \text{ or } W = Fd$$

where E_p is the gravitational potential energy, E_k is the kinetic energy, E_w or W is the work done, m is the mass, g is the gravitational field strength, h is the height, v is the velocity, F is the force applied and d is the distance travelled.

> ### Synoptic link
>
> The velocity of charged particles in an electric field can be calculated using the law of conservation of energy. See page 35.

- Energy can be transferred from one type to another. The rate at which energy is transferred is the power of a system. The equation for calculating power, P, is:

$$P = \frac{E}{t}$$

where E is the energy transferred and t is the time taken.

> ### Key terms
>
> **Law of conservation of energy** This states that while energy can change form, the total amount of energy always remains the same.
>
> **Gravitational potential energy** The amount of energy stored in an object due to its position in a gravitational field.
>
> **Kinetic energy** The amount of energy associated with an object's motion.
>
> **Work done** The energy transferred from one kind to another.
>
> **Power** How much energy is converted per second.

Do you know?

1 A car of mass 1200 kg has an engine that can supply an unbalanced force of 1.8 kN. Calculate the maximum acceleration of the car.

2 A force of 100 N is applied to an object at 30° to the horizontal. Determine the horizontal and vertical components of this force.

3 A 1.2 kg box is sitting on a ramp. The ramp makes an angle of 15° to the horizontal. Determine the component of the weight down the slope.

4 A 5.0 kg box is lying on a shelf 1.6 m above the ground. Calculate the gravitational potential energy of the box relative to the ground.

5 A 1400 kg car is travelling at a constant speed of 20 m s⁻¹ along a straight level road. Calculate the kinetic energy of the car.

6 An engine converts 24 000 J of energy in 20 minutes. What is the power of the engine?

1.3 Collisions, explosions and impulse

You need to know

- how to calculate the momentum of an object
- the principle of conservation of momentum
- how to analyse simple collisions using momentum
- how to differentiate between types of collisions using total kinetic energy
- how to use momentum to analyse explosions
- Newton's third law of motion and its effects
- how to interpret force–time graphs for interacting objects
- how to calculate impulse
- impulse is equal to change in momentum

Momentum

- All moving objects have **momentum**. It is a property of their movement. The momentum of an object is calculated using:

    $p = mv$

    where p is the momentum, m is the mass and v is the velocity.

Key term

Momentum The mass of an object multiplied by its velocity.

- Momentum is a vector quantity. You must therefore consider the direction travelled by the objects when analysing collisions and explosions.
- In the Higher physics exam, all the collisions and explosions you will be asked about will take place in a straight line. This means that you will never need to use trigonometry to solve momentum problems.

Exam tip

When analysing a collision or explosion, first decide on a sign convention. For example, 'make motion to the right positive. Then any object moving to the right has a positive velocity and momentum, and any object moving to the left has a negative velocity and momentum.

Synoptic link

Because momentum is a vector quantity, direction must be taken into account. See page 12.

Collisions

- When two objects collide, they exchange momentum.
- All collisions are subject to the **principle of conservation of momentum**: In the absence of external forces, the total momentum before the collision is equal to the total momentum after the collision.
- In a collision between two objects, A and B, this principle leads to the following equation:

$$m_A u_A + m_B u_B = m_A v_A + m_B v_B$$

where m_A is the mass of object A, m_B is the mass of object B, u_A is the velocity of object A before the collision, u_B is the velocity of object B before the collision, v_A is the velocity of object A after the collision and v_B is the velocity of object B after the collision.

- This equation can be used to analyse collisions between two objects.
- For example, a 2.0 kg trolley travelling at $1.2 \, \text{m s}^{-1}$ along a frictionless surface collides with a stationary 1.0 kg trolley.
- After the collision, the trolleys stick together and move off together, as shown in Figure 1.16.

Exam tip

If you are asked to state the principle of conservation of momentum in the exam, you must give the whole of this definition. If you miss out any words, you will not be awarded the mark.

Exam tip

The collision equation is not included on the relationships sheet you will be given before the exam, so make sure you learn it.

Figure 1.16 Before and after the collision of two trolleys

- We can use the equation to calculate the velocity of both trolleys after the collision:

$m_A = 2.0\,kg \qquad m_B = 1.0\,kg \qquad u_A = 1.2\,m\,s^{-1} \qquad u_B = 0\,m\,s^{-1}$

$v_A = v_B$ because the trollies have stuck together $= v$

$m_A u_A + m_B u_B = m_A v_A + m_B v_B$

$(2 \times 1.2) + 0 = 2v + v$

$2.4 = 3v$

$v = 0.80\,m\,s^{-1}$

Types of collisions

- Collisions are either elastic collisions or inelastic collisions.
- To determine whether a collision is elastic or inelastic, you need to calculate the *total* kinetic energy before the collision and the *total* kinetic energy after the collision and compare the two values.
- The kinetic energy, E_k, can be calculated using:

$E_k = \frac{1}{2}mv^2$

where m is the mass of the object and v is the velocity of the object.

- If the total kinetic energy before the collision is equal to the total kinetic energy after the collision, the collision is elastic.
- If the total kinetic energy before the collision is higher than the total kinetic energy after the collision, the collision is inelastic.
- Any kinetic energy that is lost will be converted into another form of energy, such as heat.
- In the example above, you can work out if the collision is elastic or inelastic.
- The total kinetic energy before the collision is:

$\frac{1}{2}mv^2 = \frac{1}{2} \times 2 \times 1.2^2 = 1.44\,J$

- The total kinetic energy after the collision is:

$\frac{1}{2}mv^2 = \frac{1}{2} \times 3 \times 0.80^2 = 0.96\,J$

- There is less total kinetic energy after the collision, therefore the collision is inelastic.

Explosions

- The principle of conservation of linear momentum also applies to explosions. This means that we can use the momentum equation to analyse what happens during an explosion:

$m_A u_A + m_B u_B = m_A v_A + m_B v_B$

Key terms

Elastic collisions Collisions in which the total kinetic energy before the collision is the same as the total kinetic energy after the collision.

Inelastic collisions Collisions in which the total kinetic energy before the collision is higher than the total kinetic energy after the collision.

Kinetic energy The energy of a moving object.

Exam tip

If you are asked to name the type of collision, you need to answer in terms of *total* kinetic energy. If you do not use the word 'total', it may not be clear which objects you are describing. If you do not use the word 'kinetic', you will not gain marks because energy is always conserved during interactions. It is only *kinetic energy* we consider when deciding whether a collision is elastic or not.

- For example, two trollies, one of mass 2.0 kg and the other of mass 1.5 kg, are stationary. One trolley releases a spring-loaded piston and the two trollies separate. The 2.0 kg trolley has an initial velocity of 6.0 m s⁻¹, as shown in Figure 1.17.

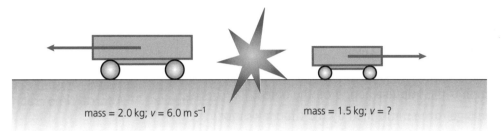

mass = 2.0 kg; v = 6.0 m s⁻¹   mass = 1.5 kg; v = ?

Figure 1.17

- You can use the principle of conservation of momentum to calculate the velocity of the second trolley after the explosion. Applying the sign convention that 'to the right is positive':

$$m_A = 2.0 \text{ kg} \qquad m_B = 1.5 \text{ kg} \qquad u_A = 0 \text{ m s}^{-1} \qquad u_B = 0 \text{ m s}^{-1}$$
$$v_A = -6.0 \text{ m s}^{-1}$$

$$m_A u_A + m_B u_B = m_A v_A + m_B v_B$$

$$0 = (2 \times -6) + 1.5 v_B$$

$$0 = -12 + 1.5 v_B$$

$$12 = 1.5 v_B$$

$$v_B = 8.0 \text{ m s}^{-1} \text{ (to the right)}$$

- In an explosion, the total kinetic energy after the explosion is greater than before. This extra kinetic energy comes from some stored energy, for example in an explosive or spring.

Newton's third law of motion and collisions

Newton's third law of motion can be applied to two objects that collide or explode apart.

- During a collision or an explosion, the forces cause a change in the momentum of an object.
- Because the forces are equal and opposite, the change in momentum of one object is equal to but opposite in sign to the change in momentum of the other object.
- In the explosion example above, the momentum of the first trolley changes by −12 kg m s⁻¹, so the momentum of the other trolley changes by +12 kg m s⁻¹.
- The forces acting on the two trollies will be the same size, but in opposite directions.

> **Synoptic link**
>
> You need to be able to analyse collisions in terms of kinetic energy. See page 15.

> **Key term**
>
> Newton's third law of motion This states that for every action there is an equal and opposite reaction. This means that when object A exerts a force on object B, object B exerts the same size force (and the same type of force) on object A, but in the opposite direction.

> **Synoptic link**
>
> Collisions can be analysed using forces. See page 12.

Force–time graphs

- If we draw the force–time graph for the forces acting on an object during a collision, we get something similar to the graph shown in Figure 1.18.
- This graph is too complex to analyse at this level, so you will be presented with something simpler in the exam, similar to the one shown in Figure 1.19.
- The area under the graph is the **impulse** acting on the object.
- The impulse is the **average force** multiplied by the time taken for the collision or explosion. Due to Newton's third law of motion, the impulse is equal to the change in momentum.
- This means that the area under a force–time graph is equal to the change in momentum of an object, as well as being equal to the impulse.
- The equation for impulse, Ft, is:

    $$Ft = mv - mu$$

- The unit for impulse is $N\,s$. $1\,N\,s$ is equivalent to $1\,kg\,m\,s^{-1}$.

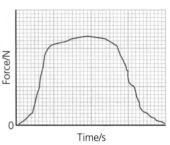

Figure 1.18 A force–time graph

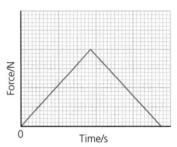

Figure 1.19 A simpler force–time graph

Do you know?

1 A ball has a mass of 0.32 kg. It is travelling at 4.0 m s⁻¹. Calculate the momentum of the ball.

2 A trolley of mass 1.2 kg is travelling at 1.6 m s⁻¹ along a frictionless surface towards a stationary trolley of mass 0.8 kg. The two trollies collide and stick together. Determine the velocity of the trollies just after the collision.

3 State the definition of an inelastic collision.

4 Two trollies are stationary on a frictionless surface. The mass of one trolley is 2.4 kg and the other is 3.0 kg. A spring-loaded piston is used to separate the two trollies so that the smaller one moves off with an initial velocity of 1.6 m s⁻¹ to the left. Determine the velocity of the larger trolley.

5 State Newton's third law of motion.

6 A ball of mass 0.16 kg travelling at 12 m s⁻¹ to the right is kicked in the opposite direction by an average force of 24 N for 0.10 seconds. Determine the new velocity of the ball.

7 The force–time graph shown in Figure 1.20 is produced during a collision.

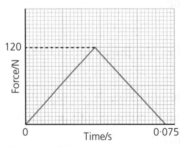

Figure 1.20

   Determine the impulse on the object.

Key term

Impulse The average force multiplied by the time the force acts for. It can be worked out from the area under a force–time graph and is equal to the change in momentum.

Exam tip

Be careful with the direction of the velocities when using this equation. If the object changes direction, u and v will have opposite signs because velocity is a vector quantity.

1.4 Gravitation

You need to know
- the horizontal and vertical motions of a projectile are independent of each other
- satellites are bodies that are in free fall around a planet or star
- how to resolve the initial velocity of a projectile into horizontal and vertical components
- how to use the horizontal and vertical components as vectors and use appropriate relationships to solve projectile problems
- how to use Newton's law of universal gravitation to solve problems involving force, masses and their separation

All bodies (objects) are under the influence of the gravitational field of a large mass. Bodies may be stationary (at rest) or have an initial velocity when they are released and be allowed to move in the gravitational field.

Gravitation

- An object that is released above the surface of the Earth, for example, will experience a force that causes it to be accelerated towards the centre of the Earth. It will accelerate (vertically downwards) at $9.8\,\mathrm{m\,s^{-2}}$ if it is relatively close to the Earth's surface.
- We can assign the acceleration to be negative because it acts in a downwards direction.
- An object launched vertically upwards will still experience an acceleration of $-9.8\,\mathrm{m\,s^{-2}}$ because it is in the Earth's gravitational field.

> ### Key term
> **Projectile** An object that is launched or released and is then acted on by only gravity and air friction.

Projectiles

- A **projectile** is an object that is usually launched at an angle to the horizontal and is then acted on by only gravity and air friction.
- Projectiles have no internal means of maintaining their motion (such as a rocket or jet engine) – for example, a struck golf ball.
- In the example of a projectile shown in Figure 1.21, you can resolve the initial velocity into its horizontal and vertical components using:

$$V_h = 55 \times \cos\theta$$

$$V_v = 55 \times \sin\theta$$

> ### Exam tip
> Make sure you can describe the motion of a projectile both if you ignore air friction and if you take air friction into account.

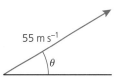

Figure 1.21

■ The horizontal component of the projectile's velocity is not affected by gravitational attraction and, therefore, you can solve most problems relating to horizontal motion using:

$s = vt$

■ Problems involving the vertical component of the velocity are more complex because they are under the influence of gravity and the velocity continually changes. You may need to use:

$v = u + at$

$s = ut + \frac{1}{2}at^2$

$v^2 = u^2 + 2as$

$s = \frac{1}{2}(u + v)t$

Synoptic link

The equations of motion are discussed on pages 5 and 6.

Satellites

■ An object projected horizontally will follow a curved path until it hits the ground. If it projected more quickly, it will travel further before it reaches the ground.
■ The time taken for an object projected horizontally to hit the ground is determined by the height from which the object is projected, not its speed.
■ Any object projected horizontally, such as a bullet, will hit the ground at the same time as an object dropped vertically from the same height.
■ As the horizontal velocity of a projectile is increased, it travels further before it hits the surface, as shown in Figure 1.22. There will come a point when the velocity is so high that the curve of the projectile's path will match the curve of the planet. At this point, the projectile will be in orbit around the planet.

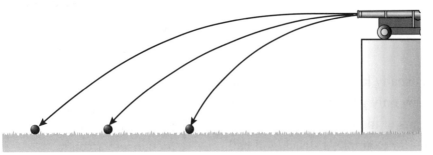

Figure 1.22

■ The velocity required to maintain orbit depends on the mass of the planet and the altitude of the **satellite** above the centre of the planet.

Key term

Satellite An object that orbits a relatively large gravitational mass, such as a planet.

- The higher the altitude, the longer it takes for the satellite to orbit the planet.
- Satellites are placed in position at the correct height and velocity for them to remain in a constant orbit. If a satellite travels too quickly, it will gradually increase its height above the planet and ultimately leave orbit. If it travels too slowly, it will gradually fall into the atmosphere and be destroyed.
- When probes are sent into deep space, it is difficult for them to reach the high velocity needed for them to travel through space relatively quickly. Fuel is heavy and difficult to transport into orbit. A probe's velocity can be increased by directing it towards planets or moons where it is 'caught' by the gravitational field of the planet and accelerates towards the planet. It then leaves the gravitational pull at a greater velocity. This is called a 'slingshot'.

Newton's law of universal gravitation

The force of attraction, F, between any two objects that have mass m_1 and m_2 and distance r between them is calculated by:

$$F = G \frac{m_1 m_2}{r}$$

where G is the gravitational constant with a value of $6.67 \times 10^{-11}\,\text{m}^3\,\text{kg}^{-1}\,\text{s}^{-2}$.

This equation describes the gravitational forces between Earth and the Sun, and Jupiter and its moons for example.

Exam tip

Make sure you do not mix up g with G. G is the universal gravitational constant and g is the gravitational field strength, which is equal to the weight of an object divided by its mass. G is constant everywhere in the universe, whereas values of g vary with location.

Do you know?

1 An object is dropped from a height of 22 m.
  a Calculate how long it takes to hit the ground.
  b Calculate the velocity with which it strikes the ground.
2 A ball is launched with a velocity of 28 m s^{-1} at an angle of 65° above the horizontal. Calculate the maximum height it could reach.
3 Calculate the gravitational attraction between a mass of 125 kg and a mass of 145 kg at a distance of 3.5 m between their centres.
4 Calculate the force of attraction between the Earth and an 85 kg person. The distance to the Earth's centre can be taken as 6370 km.
5 Describe how a satellite remains in orbit around a planet.

Key term

G The universal gravitational constant. It relates the force of attraction between masses and their separation.

1.5 Special relativity

You need to know

- the speed of light in a vacuum is the same for all observers
- measurements of space, time and distance for a moving observer are different to those experienced by a stationary observer
- these differences can be calculated using the equations for time dilation and length contraction

Special relativity

- **Special relativity** deals with the motion of objects as they travel through space and time, when the motions of the objects are at a significant fraction of the speed of light. It has two founding principles (postulates):
  1. The speed of light in a vacuum is the same for all observers.
  2. The laws of physics are identical (invariant) in all non-accelerating **frames of reference (Galilean invariance)**.
- Special relativity is 'special' only in that it applies to situations where the effect of gravity on space and time is negligible.
- The converse is general relativity, which can accommodate the effects of large gravitational fields on space and time.
- When objects travel at very high velocities, time and space can appear 'different' to those that are stationary.
- The equation that describes the relationship between the time observed by a stationary observer and the time observed by a moving observer is:

$$t' = \frac{t}{\sqrt{1-(v/c)^2}}$$

where t' is the observed time for the stationary observer, t is the observed time for the moving observer, v is the velocity of the observed object and c is the velocity of light.
- This equation refers to the effect on time measured by two observers when one observer is travelling at a velocity generally greater than 10% of the speed of light.
- Velocities greater than 10% of the speed of light are referred to as 'relativistic velocities'.

Key terms

Special relativity A theory that deals with objects moving at a constant speed faster than 10% of the speed of light.

Frames of reference All motion must be measured against something, this is known as the frame of reference.

Galilean invariance The laws of physics are the same no matter what frame of reference is used, as long as the frame of reference is not accelerating.

- The difference in the measurements of the time elapsed is referred to as **time dilation**.
- The equation shows that the observed time for a stationary observer is greater than that for a moving observer. If you travel at a relativistic velocity for any length of time, the time you experience will be less than that of a stationary observer, so you will age less.
- If we use the respective times to calculate the length of an object travelling at a relativistic velocity, the stationary observer will obtain a shorter length than the moving observer.
- This **length contraction** is given by:

$$l' = l \times \sqrt{1-(v/c)^2}$$

where l' is the length measured by the stationary observer, l is the length measured by the moving observer, v is the velocity of the observed object and c is the velocity of light.

Key terms

Time dilation The time for an event is different for observers in different frames of reference. Less time elapses for an observer in a fast-moving frame of reference than for an observer in a stationary frame of reference.

Length contraction When travelling at relativistic velocities, the length of a given object will appear to be less that when the length is measured in its own frame of reference.

How to use the equations

For example, a probe is launched and reaches a speed of $0.8c$ and 12 years have elapsed from Earth. The time elapsed by the probe can be calculated as follows:

$$t' = \frac{t}{\sqrt{1-(v/c)^2}}$$

$$t' \times \sqrt{1-(v/c)^2} = t$$

$$12 \times \sqrt{1-(0.8)^2} = t$$

$$12 \times 0.6 = t$$

$$t = 7.2 \text{ years}$$

The probe has 'aged' less than the stationary observers on Earth.

For example, an astronaut onboard a spacecraft is 1.8 m tall. The spacecraft reaches a velocity of $0.75c$. How tall would the astronaut appear from the Earth's reference frame?

$$l' = l \times \sqrt{1-(v/c)^2}$$

$$l' = 1.8 \times \sqrt{1-(0.75)^2}$$

$$l' = 1.8 \times 0.66$$

$$l' = 1.188 = 1.19 \text{ m}$$

Exam tip

Be careful about frames of reference. In this example, an observer on the spacecraft would measure the height of the astronaut as 1.8 m.

- The time dilation effect was confirmed experimentally when scientists were measuring the number of muons (sub-atomic particles) that reach Earth from cosmic ray interactions in the atmosphere.
- Both time dilation and length contraction appear unlikely, but they are physical effects of travelling at relativistic velocities and they impact on our everyday life.
- GPS systems have to account for small variations in time due to the velocities at which satellites travel and their distance from Earth.
- There are a number of other ways in which everyday things are affected by relativity, but these can be complex to explain and are not required for this course.

Exam tip

Questions on time dilation and length contraction will involve velocities greater than 10% of the speed of light. However, questions can be asked about relative motion at low velocities. For example, you could be asked about the velocity of an object relative to different frames of reference.

Example

A muon is released in the upper atmosphere at a height of 12.5 km above the Earth. It travels at a speed of 0.95c. Calculate the time it takes to reach the surface of the Earth.

$$t = \frac{s}{v} = \frac{12\,500}{0.95 \times 3.00 \times 10^8} = 4.39 \times 10^{-5}\,\text{s} = 43.9\,\mu\text{s}$$

Calculate the time elapsed as experienced by the muon.

$$t' = \frac{t}{\sqrt{1-(v/c)^2}} = 43.9 = \frac{t}{\sqrt{1-(0.95/1)^2}}$$

$$t = 43.9 \times 0.312 = t = 13.7\,\mu\text{s}$$

Do you know?

1 When an object travels at a relativistic speed, its length can contract. What speed would a 6.5 m long car need to travel at in order to fit into a 5.5 m long garage?

2 An astronaut travels at 0.35c for a mission lasting 3.75 years. What time period would have elapsed on Earth?

3 A pedestrian is walking along a moving walkway at 1.2 m s^{-1}. The walkway is moving at 0.7 m s^{-1}. Determine the speed of the pedestrian relative to the ground.

4 A spacecraft is travelling at 2.4 × 10^8 m s^{-1}. An observer on the spacecraft measures the speed of light coming from a star directly in front of the spacecraft. Determine the value for the speed of light measured by the observer.

5 Two skydivers are freefalling at a terminal velocity of 42 m s^{-1} relative to Earth. The first skydiver opens their parachute. This causes their velocity relative to Earth to become 10 m s^{-1}. Determine the velocity of the first skydiver relative to the second.

1.6 The expanding universe

You need to know

- the Doppler effect causes changes (shifts) in the wavelengths of sound and light
- how to solve problems relating to the frequencies and wavelengths emitted by moving sources
- light from retreating objects is shifted to the red region (redshift)
- how to solve problems involving redshift, wavelengths and recessional velocities
- how to solve problems involving the Hubble constant, recessional velocity and distance
- how we can determine the age of the universe
- the mass of a galaxy can be estimated by the orbital speed of stars within it
- reasons for the evidence supporting the existence of dark matter and dark energy
- the relationship between a star's emitted radiation and wavelength
- evidence supporting the theory of the Big Bang

Origins of the universe

- Observations of distant **galaxies** have shown that most galaxies are moving away from each other and that the **universe** is expanding.
- It is believed that there was a cataclysmic event around 13.7 billion years ago (the **Big Bang**) and that all matter and energy in the universe came into existence at this time.
- Space was also created at this time and the universe has been expanding ever since.

Light and stars

- Astronomers have classified the stars we can observe and have noted a certain class of star (Cephid variables).
- The light from these stars have identifiable luminosities that vary in a regular and measurable way. The periods of these variations enable astronomers to determine their average luminosities.
- This allows us to determine the distance to a star by measuring its luminosity from Earth. These stars can act as a sort of distance marker.

Key terms

Galaxy A large collection of stars, usually many billions.

Universe Everything that can be observed – matter, energy and time. It includes all the stars and galaxies, and all forms of matter and energy.

Big Bang The event in which all the universe, including time, came into existence.

The Doppler effect

- We can describe energy that is radiated using a number of terms: intensity, speed, frequency and wavelength.
- A source usually radiates energy in all directions and we can detect this using appropriate devices.
- For example, if a sound of 200 Hz is radiated, our ears and a microphone would be able to detect this.
- In this case each wave front is incident on the detector and the time between each wave front is 1/200th of a second.
- If the source of the sound moves towards us, the time between each wave front would be less than 1/200th of a second because the successive waves have a shorter distance to travel. This means more waves reach the detector each second and this leads to an increase in the frequency detected. This is the basis of the Doppler effect.
- The observed frequency, f_o, for a stationary observer is given by:

$$f_o = f_s \times \left[\frac{v}{(v \pm v_s)} \right]$$

where f_s is the source frequency, v is the wave velocity and v_s is the source velocity.

- The change in frequency is only noticeable when the velocity at which the source is moving is relatively fast in comparison to the velocity of the radiation.

Redshift

- A similar Doppler effect can be observed in the line spectra from stars and galaxies if they are moving quickly enough.
- The frequencies of the line spectra from a star that is moving away from Earth at a high velocity will be lower than the frequencies observed if the star's distance from Earth was not increasing. This move of the spectra towards a lower frequency – the red end of the spectrum – is known as 'redshift'.
- The amount by which the spectra shift is related to the velocity of the star that is moving away from Earth (recessional velocity).
- The magnitude of the redshift, z, is given by:

$$z = \frac{(\lambda_o - \lambda_r)}{\lambda_r}$$

where λ_o is the observed wavelength and λ_r is the emitted wavelength, and:

$$z = \frac{v}{c}$$

where v is the recessional velocity of the star and c is the speed of light.

Synoptic link

The inverse square law can be used to determine the distance to an object by measuring the amount of light reaching a surface. See page 47.

Exam tip

When you use this equation remember to use a negative sign for an object moving towards an observer, and a positive sign for an object moving away from the observer.

Key terms

Line spectra A pattern of lines in the light produced by stars, among other things.

Redshift The change in the pattern of the line spectra observed when viewing a moving object compared to a stationary object.

Recessional velocity The velocity of an object moving away from an observer.

Synoptic link

Line spectra are produced because of the structure of atoms. The electron shells determine which spectral lines are produced. See page 60.

■ Using these two equations we can determine the recessional velocity of a star, and therefore of galaxies, by measuring their redshift.

The Big Bang and the age of the universe

■ Astronomers, including Edwin Hubble, measured the redshift and the distance of distant galaxies (using Cepheid stars) and noted that the faster the galaxy was receding, the further away from us it was.

■ Hubble also determined that the ratio of the recessional velocity of galaxies and the distance to those galaxies was constant.

■ This led to Hubble's law:

$$v = H_0 d$$

where v is the recessional velocity, H_0 is the Hubble constant and d is the distance to the star. As of 2013, the value of $H_0 = 2.30 \times 10^{-18}\,s^{-1}$.

■ An explanation for this is the occurrence of a major event (the Big Bang) and that all matter, space and energy originated from this and has been expanding, or spreading out, ever since.

■ This also gives us a way to determine the age of the universe.

■ We have measured the recessional velocity of galaxies and the distances to them, so we have v and d. So we can calculate a value for t, which would be the time elapsed since the event occurred, using:

$$t = \frac{d}{v}$$

and, using Hubble's law:

$$\frac{d}{v} = \frac{1}{H_0}$$

this leads to:

$$t = \frac{1}{H_0}$$

■ So $1/H_0$ gives us the age of the universe – a value of around 13.7 billion years.

Exam tip

The units for the Hubble constant are given as s^{-1}. This means that when you calculate the age of the universe you will get an answer in seconds. If a question asks you for an answer in years, you will need to divide by the number of seconds in 1 year ($365.25 \times 24 \times 60 \times 60 = 31\,557\,600\,s$). Remember **not** to round off any significant figures until the final line of your calculation.

Dark matter and dark energy

- Astronomers have made estimates of the masses of galaxies by measuring galactic rotations and orbits of stars within the galaxies.
- These measurements give an indication of the motion of the galaxies, which in turn gives an indication of their mass.
- The measurements have indicated that their motion implies that there is much more mass within the galaxies than can be observed.
- This has led to the proposal that there is another type of matter, dark matter, which cannot be observed directly. It is the best way to explain the rotation of the galaxies.
- Current technologies and powerful telescopes have enabled observations of distant stars in distant galaxies.
- These observations indicate that recently (over the last few billion years), the universe's rate of expansion has been increasing.
- With no direct indication of why this is happening, scientists have proposed the existence of dark energy, which is responsible for this expansion.

> ## Key terms
>
> **Dark matter**
> A hypothetical form of matter proposed to account for the observations of the rotations of galaxies. It does not interact with electromagnetic radiation.
>
> **Dark energy** An unknown form of energy that may be responsible for the accelerated expansion of the universe.

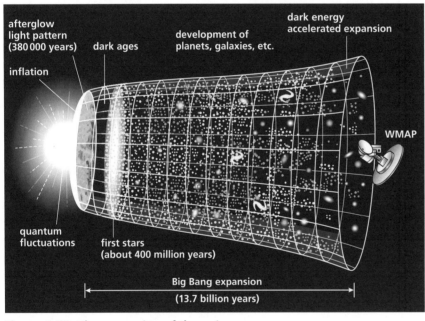

Figure 1.23 The expansion of the universe

The temperature of stellar objects

- Stars are hugely energetic bodies. They emit energy across a wide range of frequencies, from gamma rays to radio waves.
- We can deduce a lot about the nature of a star from the energy it emits.

■ It is useful to measure the frequency of and the intensity of the energy emitted from a star.

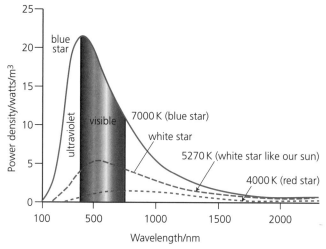

Figure 1.24 Graph of intensity of radiation against wavelength of radiation for stars

The key points to take from Figure 1.24 are:

■ The peak wavelength for hotter objects is smaller than that for cooler objects.

■ Hotter objects emit more energy (per surface area), which leads to a larger area under the graph with bigger 'spikes'.

■ Analysis of the spectra from various stellar objects can give us information about the nature and temperature of that star, and which part of the star's life cycle we are observing.

Evidence to support the Big Bang theory

■ Radiation from almost all galaxies is redshifted. This supports the evidence that the universe is expanding and (almost) all parts of the universe are moving away from each other.

■ The expansion and cooling of the universe suggests that photons characteristic of its low average temperature (in the microwave region) should be freely detectable now. This is known as cosmic microwave background radiation (CMBR).

■ Hydrogen and helium were created relatively shortly after the Big Bang and have spread throughout the universe.

■ The presence of hydrogen and helium can be identified, and their relative abundance calculated. Their abundance is in agreement with the Big Bang theory.

> **Exam tip**
>
> Make sure you can list the evidence for the Big Bang theory.

Do you know?

1. An emergency vehicle is driving along a road at $25\,\mathrm{m\,s^{-1}}$. It has a siren operating at $1350\,\mathrm{Hz}$. A vehicle on the same road is heading towards the vehicle at $15\,\mathrm{m\,s^{-1}}$. What frequency does the sound appear to the driver of the second vehicle?

2. A spacecraft of length $315\,\mathrm{m}$ is travelling at $0.85c$ relative to and towards Earth.

   a What would the length of the spacecraft be, as measured by someone on Earth?

   The spacecraft has a laser, emitting light from the front of the spacecraft.

   b What is the speed of light as measured by someone on Earth?

3. Why are Cephid variables so useful in astrophysics?

4. The peak wavelength of light emitted by stars depends on their temperature. State what happens to the peak wavelength of a star if its temperature increases.

End of section 1 questions

1. A car of mass $1200\,\mathrm{kg}$ is moving at a speed of $12\,\mathrm{m\,s^{-1}}$ along a level road.

   a Calculate the kinetic energy of the car.

   b Calculate the momentum of the car.

   The car now accelerates at $0.50\,\mathrm{m\,s^{-2}}$ for $4.0\,\mathrm{s}$.

   c Calculate the magnitude of the unbalanced force acting on the car.

   d Calculate the final speed of the car.

   e Calculate the distance travelled by the car while it is accelerating.

2. A ball of mass $2.4\,\mathrm{kg}$ travelling in a straight line at a speed of $1.2\,\mathrm{m\,s^{-1}}$ collides with another ball of mass $4.8\,\mathrm{kg}$. The second ball is stationary before the collision.

   After the collision, the first ball rebounds with a speed of $0.2\,\mathrm{m\,s^{-1}}$.

   a State the law of conservation of momentum.

   b Calculate the speed of the second ball after the collision.

   The time of the collision is $0.020\,\mathrm{s}$.

   c Calculate the change in momentum of the first ball.

   d Calculate the average force acting on the first ball during the collision.

3 The speed of sound in air is 340 m s^{-1}.

A car horn emits sound with a frequency of 1200 Hz. The car is moving away from a stationary observer at 20 m s^{-1}.

Determine the frequency heard by:

a   the driver of the car

b   the stationary observer

4 The universe is expanding as a result of the Big Bang.

a   State one piece of evidence that supports the Big Bang theory.

b   The rate of expansion of the universe is faster than physicists expected. What is responsible for this?

5 Three celestial bodies are aligned, as shown in Figure 1.25.

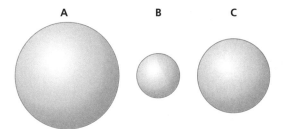

Figure 1.25

mass A = 4.65×10^{25} kg
mass B = 3.75×10^{22} kg
mass C = 5.65×10^{23} kg
distance from A to B = 5.75×10^{8} m
distance from B to C = 2.75×10^{8} m

a   Calculate the gravitational attraction between A and B.

b   Calculate the gravitational attraction between B and C.

c   Calculate the resultant force on B.

6 Muons are found in the Earth's upper atmosphere and they decay with a half-life of 2.2×10^{-6} s. They are produced when a cosmic ray proton interacts with nuclei in the upper atmosphere. They have a velocity of 0.999c.

A detector on an aeroplane detects 3450 muons in 250 s. The aeroplane is flying at a height of 2.64 km.

a   Calculate the time taken for the muons to travel to the surface of the Earth.

b   How many muons will have decayed in this time?

c   What is the time taken to travel between the aeroplane and the surface of the Earth in the muons' frame of reference?

d   What effect would this have on the number of muons detected on the surface of the Earth?

② Particles and waves

2.1 Forces on charged particles

You need to know

- charged particles experience a force in an electric field
- an electric field exists around charged particles and between charged (parallel) plates
- how to sketch the electric field patterns around and between charges and charged plates
- potential difference is defined in terms of work done and the charge
- how to solve problems involving charge, mass, speed and energy of charged particles moving in electric fields
- a moving charge produces a magnetic field
- how to determine the direction of a force on a charged particle moving in a magnetic field
- the operation of particle accelerators in terms of acceleration, collisions and deflection

Underlying physics

- Electric charge is one of the fundamental physical properties of matter. All materials contain charge.
- There are two types of charge – positive and negative.
- The area around a charged object (positive or negative) is called an **electric field**. When a charge is brought into an electric field it will experience a force.
- The direction and magnitude of this force will depend on the size of the charge, the strength of the field and whether the charge is positive or negative.

The electric fields around charges and charged parallel plates are shown in Figures 2.1 to 2.4.

Key term

Electric field An area of space in which a charged particle experiences a force.

Figure 2.1 Electric field lines around a single positive point charge

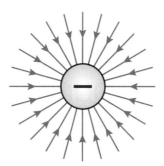

Figure 2.2 Electric field lines around a single negative point charge

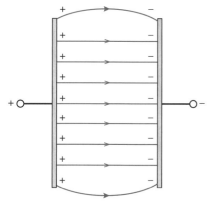

Figure 2.3 Electric field lines between oppositely charged parallel plates

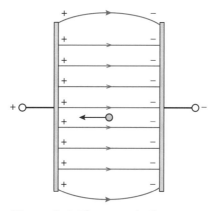

Figure 2.4 The negatively charged particle is accelerating towards one of the charged plates

- The direction of an electric field is defined as the direction of the force experienced by a positive charge.
- A positive charge will be repelled by another positive charge (or plate) and will be attracted by a negative charge (or plate).
- In diagrams, a stronger electric field is generally represented by more field lines or by the field lines being closer together.
- In Figures 2.1 and 2.2, the field lines are closer together when they are nearer the charge because this is where the field is strongest.

> ## Synoptic link
>
> Charged particles moving across a uniform electric field behave in a similar way to projectiles in a gravitational field. See page 21.

Electrical potential

- When a charge is placed in an electric field it will experience a force.
- If the charge is free to move it will accelerate.
- An energy input is required to accelerate the charge, which leads to the concept of electrical potential.
- A charge that is moved from one point in an electric field to another will have moved from a point with a certain potential to a point where the potential is probably different. For example, it may have moved closer to or further away from a positive plate.

- This leads to the term 'potential difference', which refers to the energy required to move an amount of charge (1 C) from one point to another.
- Potential difference, V, is measured in volts:

$$V = \frac{E_w}{Q}$$

where E_w is the energy supplied to the charge (in joules) and Q is the magnitude of the charge (in coulombs).
- Potential difference is one of the most common terms used when analysing electrical phenomena.

Exam tip

Make sure you know the definition of the volt. An exam question may ask for the definition of a term. These are easy marks if you have learned the definitions.

Movement of charged particles in electric fields

- An electron has a charge of -1.6×10^{-19} C and a mass of 9.11×10^{-31} kg.
- When an electron is placed between two metal plates with a potential difference of 750 V, for example, it will experience a force and be accelerated towards the positive plate.
- The energy gained by the electron, E_w, is given by:

$$E_w = QV = 1.6 \times 10^{-19} \times 750 = 1.2 \times 10^{-16} \text{ J}$$

- The velocity of the electron can be calculated using:

$$E_k = \tfrac{1}{2}mv^2$$

assuming that its starting velocity was zero.
- This gives:

$$1.2 \times 10^{-16} = \tfrac{1}{2} \times 9.11 \times 10^{-31} \times v^2$$

$$v = 1.6 \times 10^7 \text{ m s}^{-1}$$

Exam tip

In examples such as these, the charges reach high velocities in a short period of time. When calculating a velocity, make sure the answer is lower than the speed of light. A simple mistake can lead to an incorrect answer and a useful additional check is to make sure your value is less than 3×10^8 m s^{-1}.

Magnetic fields

You should be familiar with magnets and some of their effects. The magnetic fields around magnets can be described using magnetic field lines similar to those of electric fields, as shown in Figures 2.5 and 2.6.

Exam tip

Your answer to this type of question should be less than 10% of the speed of light. If it is higher than this value, you would need to take relativistic effects into account and it would state this in the question.

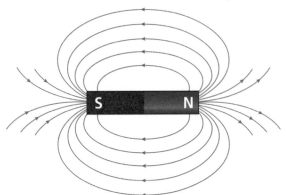

Figure 2.5 The magnetic field lines around a single bar magnet

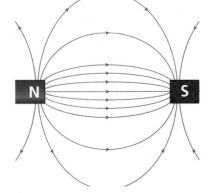

Figure 2.6 The magnetic field between two opposite poles

■ A stationary electric charge has no magnetic field, but when the charge moves a magnetic field is produced.

■ When an electric charge is placed at rest in a magnetic field, there is no measurable interaction. When the charge moves, and generates its 'own' magnetic field, these fields interact and the charge experiences a force.

■ The direction of the force on the charge depends on the direction of the magnetic field, the polarity of the charge and its direction of movement.

■ The direction of a force acting on a moving charge in an electric field is slightly more complex because the situation is three-dimensional. You first need to determine, on paper, the direction of a magnetic field for a current-carrying wire (Figure 2.7).

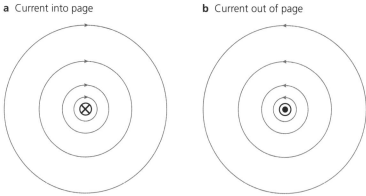

a Current into page　　　　**b** Current out of page

Figure 2.7 The 'x' shows that the current is going into the page, while the dot represents current coming out of the page

Figure 2.7 indicates:

■ the direction of a magnetic field around a current-carrying wire, with the left-hand diagram showing the current flowing *into* the page and the right-hand diagram showing the current flowing *out of* the page

■ **conventional current**, in that the charges flow from the positive to the negative terminal. It is a convention that most physicists follow.

To determine the direction of the field around a current-carrying wire, you can use the **right-hand grip rule**, as shown in Figure 2.8.

The combination of the magnetic fields results in a **force** being applied to the wire.

The effect of the combination of the current and the magnetic field can be predicted using the **left-hand rule**, as shown in Figure 2.9.

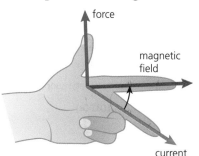

Figure 2.9 The left-hand rule

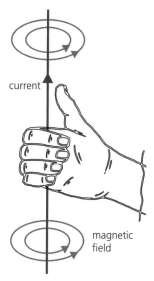

current

magnetic field

Figure 2.8 Grip the wire with your right hand so that your thumb is in the direction of the current. Your fingers will curl in the direction of the magnetic field

> **Key term**
>
> **Conventional current** The movement of positively-charged particles.

This rule operates in relation to **conventional current**. With two of the factors applied, the third will be produced.

- A current-carrying wire in a magnetic field will experience a force and then move if it is free to do so. (This is the basis of electric motors.)
- When a wire is moved in a magnetic field, a current is generated. (The basis of an electrical generator.)

Particle accelerators

- The ability to apply a force to a charge and cause it to reach high speeds is useful in physics. When particles are accelerated to high speeds and then made to collide with other particles, the resulting disintegrations can yield information about the nature of the atom and sub-atomic particles.
- The key principle is that the bombarding particles are charged. This allows the electric field to accelerate the particles to high speeds. The magnetic field generated by a moving charge allows other magnetic fields to apply a force and direct the charge to where we want it to go.

Linear accelerators

- In a linear accelerator two charged plates apply a force to a charge between them and it accelerates towards one of the plates.
- This has some limitations because the potential difference may need to be very high in order to create the high speeds.
- This can be overcome by having a series of charged plates. The particle is accelerated by one set of plates, passes through to the next set of plates, is accelerated again and so on.
- Magnetic fields keep the particles in a highly constrained 'beam', but the required length of the accelerator for high energies becomes limiting. Some linear accelerators have a length of a few kilometres.

Circular accelerators

- Circular accelerators operate by accelerating particles (using a high voltage) across a gap.
- They use strong magnetic fields to make the particles move in semi-circular paths and accelerate them back across the gap (in the opposite direction) and then repeat this again and again.
- These accelerators resemble a doughnut in that there are two large Ds with a gap between them, as shown in Figure 2.10.

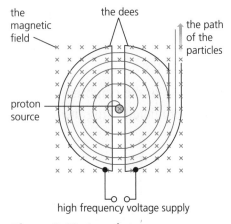

Figure 2.10 A cyclotron

Synchrotrons

A synchrotron is an accelerator in which particles are accelerated at various points in a large loop. Large magnets placed around the loop direct the particles along the loop to other accelerators and collimators, as shown in Figure 2.11. The Large Hadron Collider at CERN is an example of a synchrotron. It has a circumference of about 27 km.

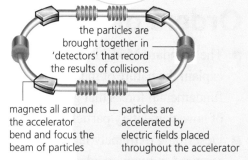

the particles are brought together in 'detectors' that record the results of collisions

magnets all around the accelerator bend and focus the beam of particles

particles are accelerated by electric fields placed throughout the accelerator

Figure 2.11 A synchrotron

Do you know?

1 Complete this sentence: Electric field lines show the direction in which a _____ charged particle will accelerate.

2 An electron is accelerated through a potential difference of 1.4 kV. Determine the kinetic energy gained by the electron.

3 A proton is accelerated by a potential difference of 3.5 kV.

If $m_p = 1.673 \times 10^{-27}$ kg and the charge on the proton = 1.60×10^{-19} C, calculate the velocity of the proton as it reaches the cathode.

4 In particle accelerators, what is the purpose of:

  a the magnetic field

  b the electric field?

Exam tip

You should know the different types of particle accelerators and be able to describe how they work.

2.2 The Standard Model

You need to know

- the Standard Model describes fundamental particles and interactions
- how to describe extremely small and extremely large physical quantities and use appropriate mathematical conventions
- that evidence for the existence of sub-atomic particles comes from the high-energy collisions produced in particle accelerators
- that every particle has an antiparticle and that the annihilation of particles is evidence for antimatter
- that the description of beta decay is evidence for the neutrino
- what fermions consist of
- hadrons are composed of quarks
- baryons are made of three quarks
- mesons are made of quark and anti quark pairs
- gravitons, photons, W- and Z-bosons and gluons are force-mediating particles

Orders of magnitude

- The Standard Model is the name given to the theory that attempts to explain the nature of matter and energy. It attempts to describe the fundamental forces that govern how particles interact and the nature of how elementary particles combine to form others.
- Describing extremely large or extremely small numbers is required in many incidences when dealing with physical phenomena. This involves being able to use scientific notation accurately and to understand the orders of magnitude represented by this notation.
- For example, the speed of light is given as $3.00 \times 10^8 \, m\,s^{-1}$ and the speed of sound in air is given as $340 \, m\,s^{-1}$. It can be difficult to compare these values when the numbers are written in different ways. Changing the way we represent the speed of sound to $3.40 \times 10^2 \, m\,s^{-1}$ makes it easier to do the comparison.
- To compare, you look at the multiplier or exponent. For the speed of light this is 10^8 and for sound in air it is 10^2. In this instance you can say that the speed of light is six orders of magnitude greater (8–2) than the speed of sound.
- In physics we use scientific notation to allow us to make comparisons with extremely small or extremely large measurements. For example:
  - $5 \times 10^{-9} \, m\,s^{-1}$ = approximate rate of growth of human hair
  - $10 \, m\,s^{-1}$ = approximate speed of an international sprinter
  - $100 \, m\,s^{-1}$ = top speed of a powerful sports car
  - $1500 \, m\,s^{-1}$ = speed of sound in water
  - $2 \times 10^8 \, m\,s^{-1}$ = speed of signal in an optical fibre

Exam tip

You will be expected to make comparisons regarding the order of magnitude of physical quantities such as speed, distance, time etc.

Sub-atomic particles and their interactions

The composition of matter is hugely complex. Early work on electrons and radioactivity has been combined with evidence from high-energy particle accelerator experiments to provide evidence for the Standard Model.

The results of these experiments have taken many years to contribute to the model, but the key points are:

- Matter particles are called **fermions** and they can be sub-divided into quarks and leptons.
- There are six types of quarks – **up, down, charm, strange, top** and **bottom**. The names mean nothing in themselves, they are simply terms. They are all fundamental particles which means they cannot be broken down into simpler, smaller particles.

Key terms

Quarks Fundamental particles that are always found combined with other quarks (or anti quarks)

Leptons Fundamental particles that can exist on their own.

Fundamental particle A particle that cannot be broken down into simpler particles.

- Quarks are categorised by their 'generation'. The differences between the generations are complex, but how they interact is similar. Higher generations have a heavier mass.
- **Leptons** include **electrons**, **muons** and **tau particles**. They have associated neutrinos. They are also fundamental particles.
- This gives us 12 fundamental particles: six quarks, three leptons and three lepton neutrinos, as shown in Table 2.1.

Exam tip

Make sure you can identify which particles are fundamental particles and which are not – for example, protons and neutrons.

Table 2.1 Matter quarks and their associated leptons

Generation	Name	Symbol	Charge	Name	Symbol	Charge	Name	Symbol	Charge	Name	Symbol	Charge
I	Up	u	$+\frac{2}{3}$	Down	d	$-\frac{1}{3}$	Electron	e	−1	Electron neutrino	v_e	0
II	Charm	c	$+\frac{2}{3}$	Strange	s	$-\frac{1}{3}$	Muon	μ	−1	Muon neutrino	v_μ	0
III	Top	t	$+\frac{2}{3}$	Bottom	b	$-\frac{1}{3}$	Tau	τ	−1	Tau neutrino	v_τ	0

Antimatter

- Each fundamental particle has an equivalent antimatter particle.
- The concept of antimatter is difficult, but it exists and is needed to explain our observations. In general antiparticles are similar to the matter particles but have opposite charges, as shown in Table 2.2.

Key term

Antimatter All fundamental matter particles have an antimatter equivalent. These have the same mass as their equivalent matter particle, but the opposite charge.

Table 2.2 Antimatter quarks and leptons

Generation	Name	Symbol	Charge	Name	Symbol	Charge	Name	Symbol	Charge	Name	Symbol	Charge
I	Anti-Up	$\bar{u}$	$-\frac{2}{3}$	Anti-Down	$\bar{d}$	$+\frac{1}{3}$	Positron	$\bar{e}^+$	+1	Anti-Electron neutrino	$\bar{v}_e$	0
II	Anti-Charm	$\bar{c}$	$-\frac{2}{3}$	Anti-Strange	$\bar{s}$	$+\frac{1}{3}$	Anti-Muon	$\bar{\mu}$	+1	Anti-Muon neutrino	$\bar{v}_\mu$	0
III	Anti-Top	$\bar{t}$	$-\frac{2}{3}$	Anti-Bottom	$\bar{b}$	$+\frac{1}{3}$	Anti-Tau	$\bar{\tau}$	+1	Anti-Tau neutrino	$\bar{v}_\tau$	0

- Antimatter particles can combine to form antimatter atoms, but these are rare. One of the challenges of physics is to explain why there is more matter than antimatter in the universe.
- Antimatter particles have been forced to collide with matter particles in accelerators and when they do, they are both annihilated. All matter is converted into energy. Both the matter particles and the antimatter particles no longer exist.

Quarks and associated particles

- A hadron is the name we give to the larger particle created when quarks are combined.
- A meson is a particle composed of a quark anti quark pair.
- A baryon is a particle composed of three quarks.
- There are rules governing how quarks can combine. These rules may seem unusual, but they are borne from years of theoretical and experimental work.
- Physicists examined the data and proposed possible explanations, and then attempted to verify the theories. We cannot justify these rules by experimentation in the classroom but they have been confirmed, as outlined in Table 2.3.

Key terms

Hadron A composite particle made up of quarks (and/or anti quarks).

Meson A composite particle made of a quark anti quark pair.

Baryon A composite particle made up of three quarks (and/or anti quarks).

Table 2.3

Particle	Description
Proton	Composed of two 'up' quarks and one 'down' quark. This gives a total charge of +1.
Neutron	Composed of two 'down' quarks and one 'up' quark. This gives a total charge of 0.
Neutrino	Close examination of the products of beta decay in the 1930s suggested that the balance of matter and energy was not correct. It was proposed there was another particle of very small mass being emitted in order to make the equation balance. This was called the neutrino. It was later confirmed in 1956.

Fundamental forces

- When examining the nature of gravitational attraction, electrostatic attraction and repulsion, and how atoms and particles are held together in the nucleus, physicists noted a range of similarities and differences in how these forces act. They categorised the forces according to their behaviour.
- There are four types of fundamental forces and each of these forces acts via force-mediating particles known as gauge bosons. There are four types of force-mediating particles. It is the exchange of these force-mediating particles that results in the force.
- The four fundamental forces, where and how they operate, and their associated force-mediating particles are shown in Table 2.4.

Key terms

Fundamental forces The four types of forces involved in the interaction of particles.

Force-mediating particles Each of the four fundamental forces has a force-mediating particle associated with it.

Table 2.4

Fundamental force	Operation	Force-mediating particle
Strong	Combines quarks to form hadrons, such as protons and neutrons, and binds protons and neutrons to form nuclei. Acts over a short range and is relatively extremely strong.	Gluon
Weak nuclear	Related to the interaction of particles that leads to radioactive decay. Weaker than the strong force (unsurprisingly) but still strong, and acts over a shorter range than the strong force.	W- and Z-bosons
Gravitational	Responsible for the attraction of all objects with mass. Relatively weak but its action is infinite in range.	Graviton (not discovered yet!)
Electromagnetic	Acts between electrically-charged particles, and in the combination of electric and magnetic fields. Has an infinite range.	Photon

■ The strong and the weak forces act over short distances, and the gravitational and electromagnetic forces have an infinite range. Figure 2.12 summarises the fundamental forces and their force-mediating particles.

Exam tip

Make sure you know the names of the fundamental forces and the force-mediating particle associated with each one.

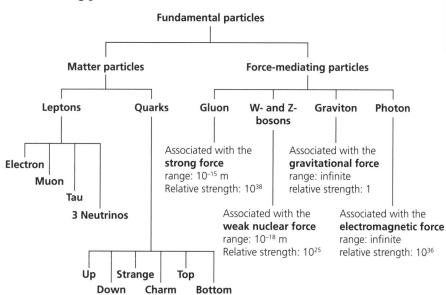

Figure 2.12

Do you know?

1 What is the difference between a baryon and a meson?
2 List the four fundamental forces and their associated force-mediating particles.
3 The distance to Proxima Centauri is 9.46×10^{15} m. The distance to Beta Orionis is 8.18×10^{18} m. By how many orders of magnitude do these distances differ?
4 How many types of quark are there?
5 Name the antiparticle of the electron.

2.3 Nuclear reactions

You need to know

■ how to use nuclear equations to describe radioactive decay, fission (spontaneous and induced) and fusion reactions, with reference to mass and energy equivalence

■ how to use appropriate relationships to solve problems involving the mass loss and the energy released by a nuclear reaction

■ $E = mc^2$

■ nuclear fusion reactors require charged particles at a very high temperature which are contained by magnetic fields

Nuclear definitions

■ We use the **atomic number** and **mass number** of an atom to identify it. Every element in the periodic table differs from other elements in that it has its own atomic number.

■ The atomic number of an element is the number of protons in the nucleus. For example, an atom of carbon has 6 protons, copper has 29 protons and lead has 82 protons.

■ The mass number of an atom is the number of its protons and neutrons combined. For example, an atom of chlorine has 17 protons and can have 18 neutrons. This is written as:

$$^{35}_{17}\text{Cl}$$

■ Chlorine atoms containing 17 protons and 20 neutrons also exist. The same element can have different mass numbers. Variations of the same element are called **isotopes**. They have the same atomic number but different mass numbers.

■ In general, elements with small atomic numbers have similar numbers of protons and neutrons. As the atomic numbers increase, the ratio of neutrons to protons increases.

■ For example, gold has 79 protons and 118 neutrons and its atomic description is:

$$^{197}_{79}\text{Au}$$

■ Radioactive decay happens when large, unstable atomic nuclei lose energy by emitting radiation, such as alpha particles, beta particles or gamma radiation.

Key terms

Atomic number The number of protons in a nucleus.

Mass number The total number of protons and neutrons in a nucleus.

Isotope The isotopes of an element have the same number of protons, but different numbers of neutrons.

Nuclear energy

- We generate some of the energy needed for our everyday electrical requirements in nuclear power stations.
- All the world's current nuclear reactors operate using **fission** reactions. The fuel for this is usually a mix of uranium and plutonium, and there are extremely serious issues with the disposal of nuclear waste and spent fuel.
- One advantage of nuclear reactors is that they produce very low carbon emissions. They are exceptionally clean in this sense.
- A **fusion** reactor could offer a cleaner and possibly cheaper way of generating electrical energy without many of the issues associated with radioactive waste. The waste product in a fusion reaction is mainly helium.
- In order for fusion reactions to occur, we need extremely high temperatures of about 10 000 000 K. Containing and managing something at this temperature is difficult.
- The hot material is in a state of matter known as a **plasma**.
- No material can withstand temperatures of such magnitude, but we can contain the plasma in a strong magnetic field, as shown in Figure 2.13.

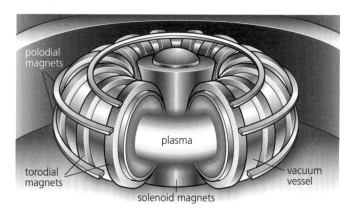

Figure 2.13 A nuclear fusion reactor

- The high temperature can overcome the repulsion the nuclei have and make them **fuse**. However, there are other serious issues in dealing with how to extract the heat from the reactor safely.

Fusion and fission

Fission

- 'Fission' describes a process in which something splits.
- A fission reaction is one in which a large nucleus is broken or split into smaller nuclei.

- As with fusion reactions, the mass of the material after the reaction is less than the mass before and this difference in mass is converted into energy.

There are two kinds of fission reactions – **spontaneous** and **induced**.

- **Spontaneous fission** refers to atoms that undergo fission naturally. Radioactive materials are examples of this. They undergo fission naturally and gradually decay until they become stable. (This can take a long time.) For example, the radioactive decay of uranium can be shown as:

$$^{238}_{92}U \longrightarrow ^{234}_{90}Th + ^{4}_{2}He$$

Spontaneous fission is really only feasible in elements with atomic numbers in the 90s or above.

- **Induced fission** refers to occasions where an atom has undergone fission, but only because of an external cause. We can cause atoms to split by introducing a neutron to the nucleus, which usually breaks down into two smaller atoms and particles. For example:

$$^{235}_{92}U + ^{1}_{0}n \longrightarrow ^{141}_{56}Ba + ^{92}_{36}Kr + 3\, ^{1}_{0}n$$

The neutrons released in this reaction could go on to cause other induced fission reactions, which in turn could go on to do the same. This is an example of a 'chain reaction' where one reaction causes other reactions to occur, and so on. This type of reaction is used in most nuclear power stations. We can control the rate of reaction by controlling the availability of the neutrons released, which cause the other reactions.

Fusion

- Atoms with a small atomic number can, under suitable circumstances, combine to form a larger atom.
- The mass of the larger atom will be less than the combined mass of the atoms before the reaction.
- This difference in the mass of the atoms before and after the reaction is converted to energy, and this is known as a **fusion reaction**. Atoms have 'fused' together to form a larger atom.
- An example of a fusion reaction is two isotopes of hydrogen – deuterium and tritium – fusing to become a helium atom and a neutron:

$$^{2}_{1}H + ^{3}_{1}H \rightarrow ^{4}_{2}He + ^{1}_{0}n$$

- In this example, the numbers involved are very small and a typical difference in mass will be of the order of 4×10^{-29} kg. This is converted to energy.

- The amount of energy released, E, can be calculated using:

    $E = mc^2$

    $E = 4 \times 10^{-29} \times (3 \times 10^8)^2 = 3.6 \times 10^{-12} \, \text{J}$

- This is a small amount of energy. However, there are vast amounts of atoms in a kilogram, for example, and this would generate huge amounts of energy.

Do you know?

1 Explain the difference between, 'spontaneous' and 'induced' fission.
2 Give two advantages of using a fusion reactor to generate electrical energy.
3 During a nuclear reaction $2.4 \times 10^{-27} \, \text{kg}$ of mass is converted into energy. Calculate the amount of energy released in this reaction.
4 Explain why a magnetic field is used to contain the plasma in a fusion reactor.

Exam tip

Be careful with the arithmetic when answering questions on nuclear reactions, for both fission and fusion. Do not round off any difference in mass part way through.

2.4 Inverse square law

You need to know
- irradiance is the power per unit area incident on a surface
- $I = P/A$
- how to use an appropriate relationship to solve problems involving irradiance, the power of radiation incident on a surface and the area of the surface
- irradiance is inversely proportional to the square of the distance from a point source
- how to use an appropriate relationship to solve problems involving irradiance and distance from a point source
- $I = \dfrac{k}{d^2}$
    $I_1 d_1^2 = I_2 d_2^2$

Radiation terms

- In physics we use some terms in a precise way. Irradiance is such a term. It is used to describe how light, or any radiated energy, is received by a surface.
- Sunlight making contact with a solar panel could be described in terms of irradiance. It is useful in this context to refer to the light

Key term

Irradiance The power incident per unit area for any type of radiation.

energy acting on the surface, rather than the energy being radiated from a source.

■ Irradiance is defined as the 'power per unit area' on a surface. This means that the unit of irradiance is watts per square metre, $W\,m^{-2}$.

■ The equation governing the irradiance on a surface, I, is:

$$I = \frac{P}{A}$$

where P is the power (in watts) and A is the area of the surface (in square metres).

■ The irradiance on a surface decreases as the distance from the source increases. This seems logical because the 'brightness' of a bulb reduces the further away you are from the bulb.

■ It is *not* a linear relationship – if you double the distance, you do not halve the 'brightness'. It is an **inverse square relationship**. This means that the irradiance is **inversely proportional to the square** of the distance from the source, as shown in Figure 2.14. In simple terms, if the distance from a point source is doubled, the irradiance is a quarter of the original irradiance.

> ## Key term
>
> **Inverse square relationship** A mathematical relationship that states when one quantity doubles, another quantity becomes a quarter of its original value.

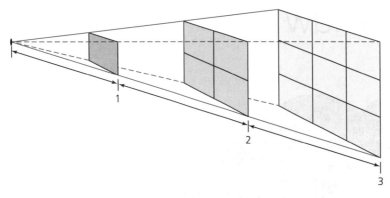

Figure 2.14

■ This can be represented mathematically by:

$$I = \frac{k}{d^2}$$

where I is the irradiance, k is a constant (calculated from the data for a given situation) and d is the distance from the source.

> ## Exam tip
>
> The **inverse square law** for irradiance only works for a point source of light. If you are asked to analyse data in the exam and find that the value of $I \times d^2$ is not constant, this means the light source is not a point source of light.

> ## Key term
>
> **Inverse square law** Many physics relationships obey this law. The magnitude of attraction for point charges or masses decreases with the square of the distance between the charges or masses.

Example

The irradiance on a surface at a distance of 2.0 m from a source is 12 W m^{-2}. The surface is moved to a distance 5.0 m from the source. Calculate the irradiance on the surface at this point.

$$I = \frac{k}{d^2}$$

$$k = I \times d^2 = 12 \times 4 = 48$$

This is the constant relating to this example.

$$I = \frac{k}{d^2}$$

$$k = I \times d^2$$

$$48 = I \times 5^2$$

$$I = \frac{48}{25} = 1.92 \text{ W m}^{-2} = 1.9 \text{ W m}^{-2}$$

A possibly simpler way of solving this is to use the relationship:

$$I_1 d_1^2 = I_2 d_2^2$$

This is nothing more than the initial equation rearranged slightly so that it makes it easier to determine the answer. It comes from:

$$I = \frac{k}{d^2}$$

For an initial set of conditions, you calculate k for the irradiance and the distance given:

$$I_1 = \frac{k}{d_1^2}$$

Rearranging gives:

$$I_1 d_1^2 = k$$

If the distance is varied and you are asked to calculate the irradiance at the new distance, the value for k does not change. Therefore:

$$k = I_2 d_2^2$$

which leads to:

$$I_1 d_1^2 = I_2 d_2^2$$

Do you know?

1 Ultraviolet light is shone onto a surface at a distance of 15 cm. The irradiance on the surface is 24 W m^{-2}. At what distance would the source have to be moved to reduce the irradiance to 3 W m^{-2}?

2 A source is placed at a distance x from a surface. It is then moved to a distance of $10x$ from the surface. How does the irradiance compare now?

3 A solar panel has an area of 20 m^2 and 9600 J of light energy is incident on the panel per minute. Determine the irradiance of the light on the panel.

4 At a distance of 0.20 m from a bulb, the irradiance is 600 W m^{-2}. The bulb is replaced by a new bulb with four times the power of the first bulb. At what distance from the new bulb is the irradiance 6.0 W m^{-2}?

2.5 Wave–particle duality

You need to know

- why the photoelectric effect shows that light has a particle nature
- light is made up of photons
- photons of sufficient energy can eject electrons from the surfaces of some materials (metals)
- the minimum energy required to eject an electron from a metal surface is called the work function
- the minimum frequency of light required to eject an electron from a metal surface is called the threshold frequency
- how to solve problems using the equation $E = hf$
- the maximum kinetic energy of an ejected electron is the energy of the photon minus the work function of the metal

The photoelectric effect

The photoelectric effect can be demonstrated using the apparatus shown in Figure 2.15.

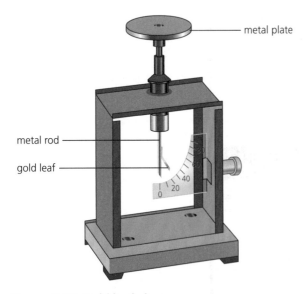

Figure 2.15 **Gold leaf electroscope**

- When the metal plate on top of the gold leaf electroscope is charged, the gold leaf is deflected and gives a reading on the scale.
- The metal plate can be charged positively or negatively. In either case, the gold leaf is deflected.
- If the metal plate is positively charged, it will *not* discharge when ultraviolet radiation or visible light is shone onto it.

- If the metal plate is negatively charged, it will *not* discharge when visible light is shone onto it. However, it *will* discharge when ultraviolet radiation is shone onto it.
- These results are summarised in Table 2.5.

Table 2.5

Charge on plate	Type of incident *e/m* radiation	Result
Positive	Visible	No effect
Positive	Ultraviolet	No effect
Negative	Visible	No effect
Negative	Ultraviolet	Discharges

- The explanation for these results is that beams of electromagnetic radiation are not continuous waves but are made up of individual packets of energy called photons.

- No matter how bright the white light is, each individual photon does not have sufficient energy to remove a single electron from the metal plate, so it can never be discharged by white light.
- However, each individual photon of ultraviolet light has enough energy to remove one electron from the plate. This means that even a low irradiance of ultraviolet on a negatively-charged plate will make the metal discharge its excess electrons.
- The energy of each photon, E, (in joules) is given by:

$$E = hf$$

where h is Planck's constant (6.63×10^{-34} J s) and f is the frequency (in hertz).

- The photoelectric effect suggests that light has a particle nature. Light is said to be quantised. This means that is made up of individual packets, photons.

Synoptic link

It is important to realise that light has both a particle nature and a wave nature. See page 54.

Work function

Every material has a minimum energy that will cause an electron to be ejected from its surface. This is called its work function, W. If a photon has less energy than the work function of a material, it cannot eject any electrons. If a photon has more energy than the work function of a material, it will eject an electron from the material.

Work function varies from material to material. If you require this in the exam, you will be given its value. For metals, in general,

Key term

Photon An individual packet of light energy.

Exam tip

In an exam, it is quite common to be given the wavelength of light rather than its frequency. You can calculate the frequency using:

$$v = f\lambda$$

where v is the speed of light (3×10^8 m s^{-1}).

Exam tip

Make sure you can explain the photoelectric effect in terms of one photon causing one electron to be ejected from a metal plate. This shows the quantisation of light.

Key term

Work function The minimum energy that a photon must have in order to eject an electron from a material.

the more reactive a metal is the lower its work function. Table 2.6 shows some examples.

Table 2.6

Metal	Work function
Copper	7.53×10^{-19} J
Aluminium	6.54×10^{-19} J
Magnesium	5.90×10^{-19} J
Calcium	4.65×10^{-19} J

Threshold frequency

- Because there is a minimum energy required to eject an electron, there must be a minimum frequency that a photon needs to have before it can eject an electron from the material. This is called the **threshold frequency**.
- If a photon has a frequency lower than the threshold frequency, it can never eject an electron from the material.
- The threshold frequency, f_0, and the work function, W, are related by the equation:

$$W = hf_o$$

Kinetic energy of ejected electrons

- Electrons that are ejected from a plate are called **photoelectrons**. These photoelectrons will have kinetic energy because they are moving.
- The maximum kinetic energy of the photoelectrons is the difference between the energy of the incident photon and the work function of the material, given by:

$$E_k = E - W$$

$$E_k = hf - hf_o$$

$$E_k = h(f - f_o)$$

- This shows that the maximum kinetic energy of the photoelectrons depends on the difference between the frequency of the photon and the threshold frequency multiplied by Planck's constant.

Key term

Threshold frequency
The minimum frequency required to eject an electron from a negatively-charged material.

Exam tip

The equation $W = hf_o$ does not appear on the relationships sheet for the exam. This is because it is a special case of the equation $E = hf$.

Key term

Photoelectrons Electrons that have been ejected from a plate by the action of photons during the photoelectric effect.

Exam tip

Do not confuse 'photons' with 'photoelectrons'. Photons make up the beam of radiation striking a surface. Photoelectrons are ejected from the charged material.

Do you know?

1 Explain how the photoelectric effect shows that light has a particle nature.

2 State the name of the minimum energy required to eject an electron from a negatively-charged plate.

3 What is meant by the 'threshold frequency' of a material?

4 A beam of monochromatic light has a wavelength of 620 nm. Determine the energy of a photon of light in this beam.

5 The work function of sodium is 2.91×10^{-19} J. Determine the threshold frequency of sodium.

6 The threshold frequency for a metal is 1.04×10^{15} Hz. Photons with a frequency of 1.25×10^{15} Hz are incident on the metal. Determine the maximum kinetic energy of a photoelectron emitted by the metal.

2.6 Interference

You need to know

- coherent waves have a constant phase relationship
- interference is evidence for the wave nature of light
- how to describe constructive and destructive interference in terms of the phase difference between two waves
- constructive interference takes place when the path difference between two coherent waves is zero or a whole number of wavelengths
- destructive interference takes place when the path difference between two coherent waves is an odd number of half wavelengths
- how to solve problems using $m\lambda = S_1P - S_2P$
- how to solve problems using the diffraction grating equation $m\lambda = d \sin \theta$

Phase and coherence

- 'Phase' is a way of describing and comparing two waves.
- When waves are in phase, the **crests** correspond with crests and **troughs** correspond with troughs, as shown in Figure 2.16.
- When waves are exactly out of phase, the crests correspond with troughs, as shown in Figure 2.17.

Coherent waves have a constant phase relationship. This does not mean that the waves are in phase with each other. It means that the phase difference does not change.

Key terms

Crest A maximum point on a wave.

Trough A minimum point on a wave.

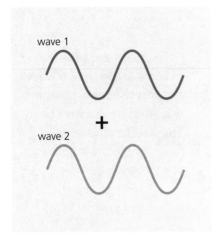

Figure 2.16 **Waves in phase**

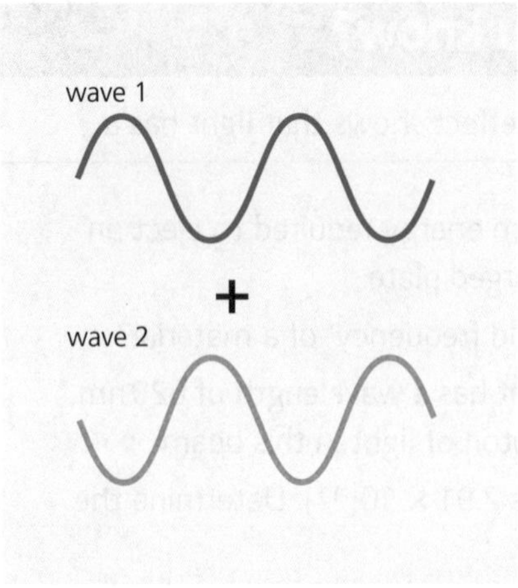

Figure 2.17 **Waves out of phase**

- The two waves in Figure 2.18 are not in phase but they are coherent.

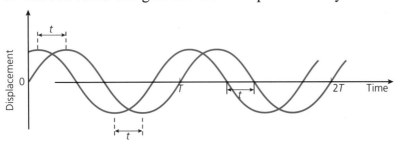

Figure 2.18 **Coherent waves**

Interference

- When coherent waves meet they produce an **interference** pattern.
- Figure 2.19 shows the interference pattern produced in a ripple tank filled with water.

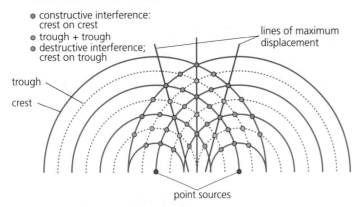

Figure 2.19 **An interference pattern in a ripple tank**

- When two waves that are in phase meet they produce **constructive interference**, as shown in Figure 2.20. Where a crest meets a crest, it produces a larger crest. Where a trough meets a trough, it produces a deeper trough.

Exam tip

Ensure you understand the definition of 'coherent'.

Key terms

Interference This can occur when two waves meet. The effect of two coherent sets of waves crossing will depend on their phase differences as they meet at various points. If an interference effect is observed, it proves that waves are involved.

Constructive interference This takes place where waves that are in phase meet.

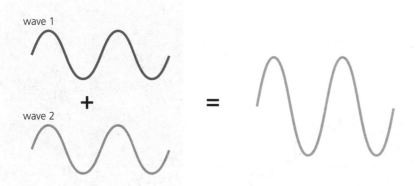

wave 1

wave 2

+ =

Figure 2.20 Because the maxima of these two waves occur at the same time, they will interfere constructively. The resultant wave will have double the amplitude of each single wave

- When two waves meet exactly out of phase they produce destructive interference, as shown in Figure 2.21. Where a crest meets a trough, they cancel each other out.

Key term

Destructive interference Happens where waves that are exactly out of phase meet.

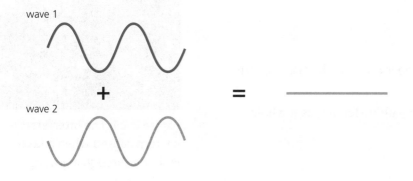

wave 1

wave 2

+ =

Figure 2.21 The maximum of one wave occurs at the same point as the minimum of the other and the waves cancel each other out. Both waves still exist and will continue after this point

- Only waves produce interference. Interference is the test for wave properties.

Path difference

- For an interference pattern to be produced (see Figure 2.22) there must be at least two coherent sources of waves.
- The distance from one source to a point in the pattern is called a path length. The difference in distance from one source to a point in the pattern and a second source to the same point in the pattern is called the path difference.
- The path difference is a distance and is given by the equation:

    path difference = $S_2P - S_1P$

    where S_1P is the distance from source 1 to a point in the pattern, and S_2P is the distance from source 2 to the same point in the pattern.
- At a point of constructive interference in the pattern, the path difference must either be zero or a whole number of wavelengths. At a point of destructive interference, the path difference must be an odd number of half wavelengths.

Exam tip

If you are asked how interference is produced, make sure you say that the waves 'meet'. For example, if you are asked how constructive interference takes place, make sure your answer includes 'waves meet in phase'.

Key term

Path difference The difference in distance from one source of waves to a given point in the interference pattern and the distance from a second source to the same point.

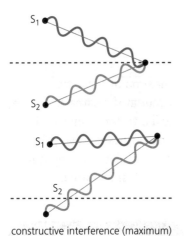

constructive interference (maximum)　　　　destructive interference (minimum)

Figure 2.22 Waves combining and interfering

■ For constructive interference, the path difference is a whole number of wavelengths:

$$m\lambda = S_2P - S_1P$$

where m is zero or a whole number and λ is the wavelength of the wave.

■ For destructive interference, the path difference is a whole number of half wavelengths:

$$(m + \tfrac{1}{2})\lambda = S_2P - S_1P$$

where m is zero or a whole number and λ is the wavelength of the wave.

Interference of light

■ When light is shone through a grating, the pattern shown in Figure 2.23 is observed.
■ This is called an interference pattern. It shows that light has a wave nature.
■ This means that light can behave both as a wave and a particle. This gives rise to the idea of **wave–particle duality**.

In this section, you will look at the wave properties of light.

■ As you have seen, when a laser is shone through a grating, an interference pattern is produced. Laser light is **monochromatic**.

Figure 2.23 The interference pattern caused when a laser is shone through a grating

Synoptic link

It is important to realise that light has both a wave nature and a particle nature. See page 50.

Key terms

Wave–particle duality
There are times when light behaves as a wave (for example, interference) and others when it behaves as a particle (for example, the photoelectric effect). We say it has a dual nature.

Monochromatic One colour only.

■ The pattern produced is described by the equation:

$$m\lambda = d\sin\theta$$

where m is the order of the maximum, λ is the wavelength of the light, d is the distance between two lines on the grating and θ is the angle between the central maximum and the maximum being considered, as shown in Figure 2.24.

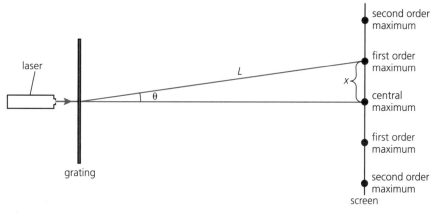

Figure 2.24 **Experiment to determine the wavelength of a laser light passing through a grating**

Do you know?

1 State what is meant by the term 'coherent'.

2 Describe in terms of waves how a point of destructive interference is formed.

3 A maximum forms at a point in a sound interference pattern 0.48 m from one speaker and 0.12 m from another speaker.

  a Calculate the path difference.

  b Determine which of the following wavelengths could be the wavelength of the sound waves:

  0.12 m

  0.24 m

  0.36 m

  0.48 m

4 A grating has 1000 lines per millimetre. Determine the slit separation on the grating (in m).

5 Light from a laser of wavelength 620 nm is shone onto a grating with a slit separation of 5.0×10^{-6} m. Determine the angle made to the second order maximum.

2.7 Spectra

You need to know

- how to describe the Bohr model of the atom
- what is meant by the terms 'ground state', 'energy levels', 'ionisation' and 'zero potential energy' in relation to the Bohr model of the atom
- how line emission spectra, continuous emission spectra and absorption spectra are produced in terms of electron energy level transitions
- how to solve problems involving energy levels and the frequency of the radiation emitted/absorbed
- how to solve problems using $E_2 - E_1 = hf$ and $E = hf$
- absorption lines in the spectrum of sunlight provide evidence for the composition of the Sun's outer atmosphere

The Bohr model of the atom

The Bohr model of the atom has four main features:

1. The atom has a central positively-charged **nucleus**.
2. **Electrons orbit** the nucleus in fixed paths.
3. Only certain energy levels for electrons are allowed in the atom.
4. When an electron moves from one energy level to another, it will either absorb or emit a specific amount of energy (a photon).

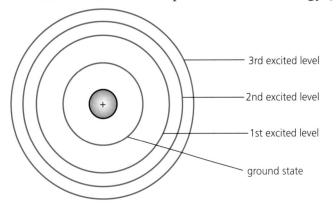

- 3rd excited level
- 2nd excited level
- 1st excited level
- ground state

Figure 2.25 A simple model of an atom showing the central nucleus and the orbits (or energy levels) around it

Energy levels in the Bohr model

- The lowest energy level that an electron can occupy in the atom is called the **ground state**.
- When an electron is in a higher energy level, it is said to be in an **excited state**.

Key terms

Nucleus The core of the atom. It is very small but is dense and contains protons and neutrons. Nearly all the atom is empty space.

Electron orbits The paths in which electrons can move around the nucleus. They are also referred to as electron shells and energy levels.

Exam tip

Be careful not to confuse the Bohr model and the Rutherford model of the atom. It is the Bohr model that you need to know for this course.

Key terms

Ground state The lowest energy level an electron can occupy inside the atom.

Excited state When an electron is in an energy level higher than the ground state.

- The **ionisation** level is where an electron gains enough energy to escape from the atom. At this point the electron has zero potential energy. This means that the energy levels inside the atom have negative values.

Electron energy transitions

- The electron orbits inside the atom can be described as **electron energy levels**.
- The electron energy levels inside the hydrogen atom are normally represented as shown in Figure 2.26. The energy values are negative because when an electron is removed from the atom it has zero potential energy.

E_4 ——— -0.871×10^{-19} J

E_3 ——— -1.36×10^{-19} J

E_2 ——— -2.42×10^{-19} J

E_1 ——— -5.45×10^{-19} J

E_0 ——— -21.8×10^{-19} J

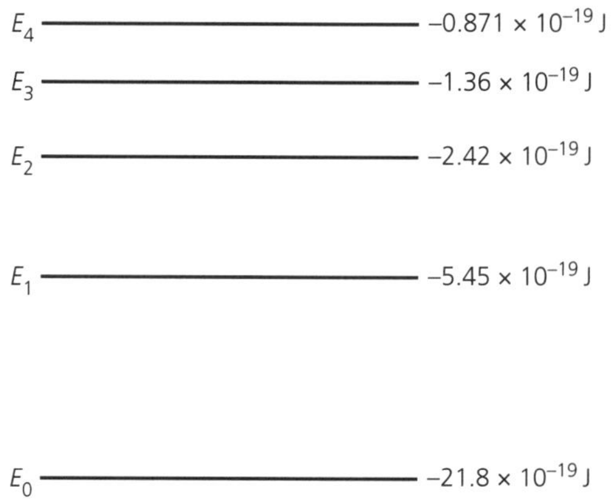

Figure 2.26 **Electron energy levels inside the hydrogen atom**

- In this diagram, E_0 is the ground state. Electrons can make a transition between any two levels inside the atom. This means that there are 10 possible **electron energy transitions** in this atom (E_4 to E_3, E_4 to E_2, E_4 to E_1, and so on).
- Each of these electron energy transitions has a specific amount of energy associated with it – the difference between the energies of the two levels. For example, when an electron moves from E_3 to E_1, the difference between the two energy levels is:

$$E_3 - E_1 = -1.36 \times 10^{-19} - (-5.45 \times 10^{-19}) = 4.09 \times 10^{-19} \text{ J}$$

- This means that every time an electron moves from E_3 to E_1, 4.09×10^{-19} J of energy is released. This energy will be released in the form of a photon.
- The frequency of this photon can be found using:

$$E = hf$$
$$f = \frac{E}{h} = \frac{4.09 \times 10^{-19}}{6.63 \times 10^{-34}} = 6.17 \times 10^{14} \text{ Hz}$$

- All the photons produced by the E_3 to E_1 transition will have this frequency.

- Because there are only ten possible transitions in this atom, it can produce photons of ten frequencies. This means that a **line emission spectrum** will be produced.
- The energy level transition with the biggest difference in energy will produce the photon with the highest frequency.
- Based on the following equation, the energy level transition with the smallest difference in energy will produce the photon with the longest wavelength:

$$\lambda = \frac{v}{f}$$

where v is the speed of light.

Emission spectra

- Because the light coming from a particular type of atom is quantised – the energy levels inside the atom mean that only certain energy transitions are possible and so only photons with these energies can be produced – each type of atom produces a spectrum made up of lines.
- Each of the lines corresponds to a particular energy transition. Because every type of atom has a set of different energy levels, the line spectrum for each type of atom is different. Figures 2.27 and 2.28 show two examples of spectra.

Figure 2.27 The visible spectrum for hydrogen

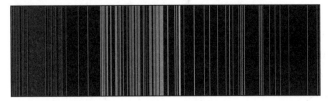

Figure 2.28 The visible spectrum for iron

- You can see that the line spectrum for iron is more complex than the spectrum for hydrogen. This is because there are significantly more energy levels in an iron atom than in a hydrogen atom.

Absorption spectra

- If a beam of white light is shone through a vapour of a gas, some of the photons in the beam are absorbed by the vapour.
- These photons have the same energy as the gap between two energy levels in the atoms of the gas. The photons that have exactly the correct amount of energy cause electrons to move from lower

energy levels to higher ones. These are the only ones that are absorbed and this produces an **absorption spectrum**. Figure 2.29 shows an example of this.

Figure 2.29 The absorption spectrum for hydrogen

If you compare the emission spectrum for hydrogen and the absorption spectrum for hydrogen, you can see that the lines are in exactly the same place. This is due to the energy levels inside the atom.

- When an electron falls from one energy level to another, it emits a photon with energy equal to the difference in energy between the two levels.
- When a photon is absorbed, it must have exactly the same energy as the difference between the two energy levels. Because the photons being emitted or absorbed have the same energy, they must also have the same frequency:

$$E = hf$$

where h is Planck's constant.

The Sun's atmosphere

- When light from the Sun is analysed using a spectrometer dark lines are observed, as shown in Figure 2.30.

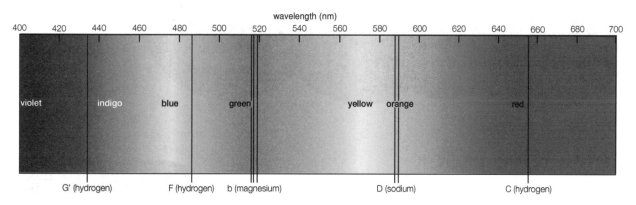

Figure 2.30 The dark lines in the emission spectrum of light from the Sun

- These lines are caused by the absorption of photons of light by atoms in the outer atmosphere of the Sun. Each absorbed photon has the same energy as the energy gap between two energy levels in a specific kind of atom.
- When these lines are analysed, it is possible to identify which elements are present in the Sun's outer atmosphere.

Do you know?

1 Describe four features of the Bohr model of the atom.

2 What is the name of the lowest energy level that an electron can occupy?

3 Describe how one of the lines is produced in the line emission spectrum of hydrogen.

4 State what the absorption lines in the Sun's spectrum are evidence of.

5 An electron falls from one energy level to another in a hydrogen atom. The difference between the energy levels is 1.06×10^{-19} J. Calculate the frequency of the photon emitted.

6 One of the absorption lines in the Sun's spectrum occurs at 520 nm. Determine the difference in energy between the two energy levels when a photon of this wavelength is absorbed.

2.8 Refraction of light

You need to know

- the definition of the absolute refractive index of a medium is the ratio of the speed of light in a vacuum to the speed of light in the medium
- how to solve problems using $n = \dfrac{\sin \theta_1}{\sin \theta_2}$
- how to describe an experiment to determine the refractive index of a medium
- how to solve problems using $n = \dfrac{\sin \theta_1}{\sin \theta_2} = \dfrac{v_1}{v_2} = \dfrac{\lambda_1}{\lambda_2}$ and $v = f\lambda$
- the refractive index of a medium increases as the frequency of light increases
- the critical angle of a medium is the angle of incidence that causes light to refract at 90° to the normal
- total internal reflection takes place when the angle of incidence is greater than the critical angle
- how to solve problems using $\theta_c = \dfrac{1}{n}$

Refractive index

- When light travels from one transparent medium to another, its speed changes. For example, when light moves from air to water it slows down.
- The ratio of the speed of light in a vacuum to the speed of light in the medium is known as the **absolute refractive index** of the medium. This is a constant for a given material.

Key term

Absolute refractive index The ratio of the speed of light in a vacuum to the speed of light in a given material.

- Because the speed of light in air is almost the same as the speed of light in a vacuum, a refractive index is usually measured when light moves from air into a material.
- Refractive index is a ratio, so it does not have any units.
- When light strikes the surface of a material obliquely, this change in speed causes it to change direction. Figure 2.31 shows an example of this.

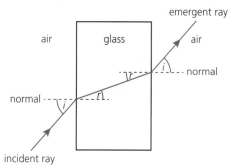

Figure 2.31 Refraction of light in a glass block

- Note that angles are always measured from a **normal**.
- The ray of light that enters the block is called the **incident ray** and the angle it makes with the normal in air is called the **angle of incidence**, i.
- The ray of light inside the block is called the **refracted ray** and the angle it makes with the normal in the block is called the **angle of refraction**, r.
- You need to be able to describe how to carry out an experiment to measure the refractive index of a material.
- Using the set up shown in Figure 2.31, a ray of laser light is shone into the block at different angles of incidence and the corresponding angles of refraction are measured.
- These results are then processed to find the sine of the angles of incidence and the sine of the angles of refraction.
- When a graph of the results is drawn it is a straight line through the origin, as shown in Figure 2.32.
- This means that the sine of the angle of incidence is proportional to the sine of the angle of refraction.
- The slope of the line is the refractive index of the material, n, and is given by:

$$n = \frac{\sin i}{\sin r}$$

which is often written as:

$$n = \frac{\sin \theta_1}{\sin \theta_2}$$

where θ_1 is the angle in air and θ_2 is the angle in the material.

Key terms

Normal A line drawn at right angles to a surface.

Incident ray The incoming ray of light. This is often, but not always, a ray of light in air.

Angle of incidence The angle between the incident ray of light and the normal.

Refracted ray The ray of light inside the material.

Angle of refraction The angle between the refracted ray and the normal.

Exam tip

Be careful with diagrams in the exam. Sometimes you are given the angle from the normal and sometimes you are given the complementary angle. Make sure you always use the angle from the normal to the ray of light.

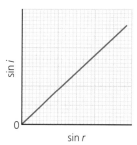

Figure 2.32

Refractive index and wavelength

- When light moves from one medium to another, its frequency stays the same.
- Based on the following equation, you know that when the speed changes and the frequency remains the same, the wavelength must change:

$$v = f\lambda$$

which can be rearranged to give:

$$f = \frac{v}{\lambda}$$

- This shows that frequency is the ratio of speed to wavelength. As the frequency stays constant, the ratio of v to f must also stay constant. If, for example, the speed halves the wavelength must also half.
- When light travels from one medium to another:

$$f_1 = f_2$$
$$\frac{v_1}{\lambda_1} = \frac{v_2}{\lambda_2}$$
$$\frac{v_1}{v_2} = \frac{\lambda_1}{\lambda_2}$$

- The absolute refractive index of a material, n, has already been defined as the ratio of the speed of light in a vacuum to the speed of light in the material.
- This means that n must also be equal to the ratio of the wavelength of the light in a vacuum to its wavelength in the material:

$$n = \frac{\lambda_1}{\lambda_2}$$

- We can now combine all the equations for absolute refractive index to give:

$$n = \frac{\sin \theta_1}{\sin \theta_2} = \frac{v_1}{v_2} = \frac{\lambda_1}{\lambda_2}$$

Refractive index and frequency

- When white light travels through a prism it produces a spectrum, as shown in Figure 2.33.
- This effect is known as dispersion. You can see that blue light is refracted more than red light. Blue light has a higher frequency than red light.
- The refractive index of blue light for any material is higher than the refractive index of red light for the same material.

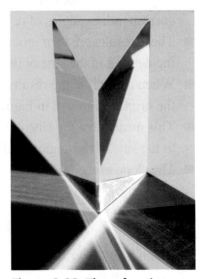

Figure 2.33 The refractive index of a material is dependent on the frequency of the light. This is why a prism can disperse white light into different colours

Critical angle and total internal reflection

- When light travels from glass into air, it refracts away from the normal.
- An incident angle is reached when the ray of light refracts at 90° to the normal. When this happens the angle of incidence in the glass is called the **critical angle** of the glass, as shown in Figure 2.34.

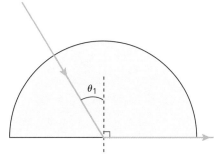

Figure 2.34 The angle of incidence is at the critical angle. The light is refracted at exactly 90°

- You can use the equation for refractive index to derive an equation for a critical angle. The angle in air, θ_1, is 90°, so $\sin\theta_1$ equals 1. θ_2 is the critical angle, θ_c.

$$n = \frac{\sin \theta_1}{\sin \theta_2} = \frac{1}{\sin \theta_c}$$

or

$$\sin \theta_c = \frac{1}{n}$$

- If the light inside the block strikes the surface at an angle to the normal greater than the critical angle, none of the light emerges from the block at this surface, as shown in Figure 2.35.

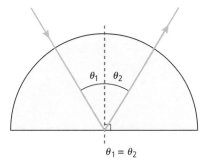

$\theta_1 = \theta_2$

Figure 2.35 The angle of incidence in this case is greater than the critical angle, so there is no longer an angle of refraction. All the light is internally reflected

- In this case, we say that the light is **totally internally reflected**. Total internal reflection is when all the ray of light is reflected at the material's boundary so that none of it emerges.

Do you know?

1 State the definition of the absolute refractive index of a material.

2 The refractive index of a particular type of glass is 1.43. A ray of light strikes the glass–air boundary at 25° relative to the normal. Determine the angle of refraction in this glass.

3 A ray of light has a frequency of 5.2×10^{14} Hz. It enters a block of glass that has a refractive index of 1.28. Determine the frequency of this light in the glass block.

4 The refractive index of water is 1.33. The wavelength of red light in air is 656 nm. Determine the wavelength of this light in water.

5 State the definition of 'critical angle'.

6 The refractive index of yellow light in diamond is 2.42. Calculate the critical angle of this light in diamond.

End of section 2 questions

1 An electron is accelerated from rest through a potential difference of 480 V.

   a What is meant by a potential difference of 480 V?

   b Determine the gain in kinetic energy of the electron?

   c What is the final velocity of the electron?

2 a An electron is a lepton. Why is an electron described as a fundamental particle?

   b A proton is a baryon. How many quarks does a proton contain?

   c How many quarks does a meson contain?

   d Name the four fundamental forces.

   e Which force is mediated by gluons?

3 Single-celled animals such as amoeba are about 300 µm in length. Blue whales can grow to be 30 m in length. How many orders of magnitude is the blue whale bigger than an amoeba?

4 Water has a refractive index of 1.33.

   a A ray of monochromatic light inside some water strikes the surface at an angle of 12° relative to a normal. Determine the angle the ray of light makes to the normal as it emerges into the air.

   b The ray of light has a wavelength of 520 nm in air. Determine the wavelength of this light in water.

   c Determine the frequency of the light in:

   i air

   ii water

   d Define 'critical angle'.

   e Determine the critical angle for this light in water.

5 Explain what is meant by 'constructive interference':

   a   in terms of waves

   b   in terms of path difference

6 Light is shone onto a clean strip of magnesium. The work function of magnesium is 5.90×10^{-19} J. The kinetic energy of the ejected photoelectrons is 2.52×10^{-19} J. Calculate:

   a   the frequency of the light shone onto the magnesium

   b   the wavelength of the light shone onto the magnesium

   c   the maximum velocity of the ejected electrons

7 A small solar cell is positioned at a distance of 2.5 m from a point source. It produces an output of 1.75 V at this point.

   a   Calculate its output voltage at a distance of only 1.1 m from the source.

   b   At what distance from the cell would it supply 0.55 V?

8 A nuclear reaction is represented as shown:

$$^{238}_{92}U \rightarrow \, ^{234}_{90}Th + \, ^{4}_{2}He$$

   mass of $^{238}U = 3.983 \times 10^{-25}$ kg

   mass of $^{234}Th = 3.887 \times 10^{-25}$ kg

   mass of $^{4}He = 6.642 \times 10^{-27}$ kg

   Calculate the energy released during this reaction.

9 Explain the difference between an 'induced' nuclear reaction and a 'spontaneous' nuclear reaction.

10 A medical laser has of power 1.75 W and frequency of 6.55×10^{18} Hz. When used in treatment, it emits energy in pulses and each pulse lasts for 0.075 s.

   a   Calculate the wavelength of the light.

   b   How much energy is associated with each photon?

   c   How much energy is transferred in each pulse?

3.1 Monitoring and measuring AC

You need to know

- AC is a type of current that changes direction
- the instantaneous value of an AC changes with time
- what is meant by the peak and root mean square (rms) values of current and potential difference (voltage)
- the relationship between peak and rms values
- how to measure the peak potential difference and the frequency of an AC supply
- how to solve problems using $V_{rms} = \dfrac{V_{peak}}{\sqrt{2}}$ and $I_{rms} = \dfrac{I_{peak}}{\sqrt{2}}$ and $T = \dfrac{1}{f}$

Alternating current

- Alternating current (AC) is constantly changing in both direction and value. Most AC that you will meet take the form of a sine wave, as shown in Figure 3.1.

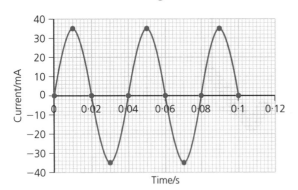

Figure 3.1 **A graph of AC against time**

- The maximum current (both positive and negative) is known as the **peak current**, I_{peak}. In this case, the peak current is 35 mA.
- The **period**, T, of the current is the time taken for one complete cycle. In this case, it is 0.04 s.
- The voltage of an AC follows a similar pattern, as shown in Figure 3.2.

Key terms

AC Alternating current – the direction and value of an alternating current change with time.

Peak current The maximum current from an AC supply.

Period The time for one complete AC cycle.

- In this case, the **peak voltage** is 2.5 V.

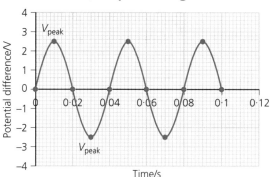

Figure 3.2

Peak and root mean square

- When we give the value for current or potential difference (voltage) in an AC circuit, we state the values that are equivalent to those in a direct current (DC) circuit.
- Because an AC varies, its value is not constant. We therefore have to state an average value.
- The arithmetic average of both the current and potential difference are zero, because all the positive values are cancelled out by negative values. To overcome this we use the **root mean square** (rms) value. Mathematically, we square all the values (so all the negative values become positive), find the mean (average) and then take the square root of that value. This sounds complicated, but for a sine wave the rms value is simply the peak value divided by the square root of two:

$$V_{rms} = \frac{V_{peak}}{\sqrt{2}}$$

$$I_{rms} = \frac{I_{peak}}{\sqrt{2}}$$

Measuring AC

- You can work out the rms potential difference and frequency from an oscilloscope pattern, as shown in Figure 3.3.

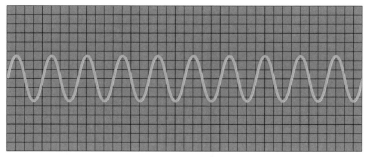

Figure 3.3 The trace on an oscilloscope screen (each square is 1 cm)

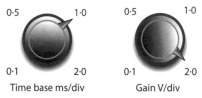

Time base ms/div Gain V/div

Figure 3.4 The settings on an oscilloscope

- You can think of the trace pattern as a graph, with time in the x-direction and voltage in the y-direction.
- The time base setting (Figure 3.4) shows how many seconds each division is worth. In this case each division is equivalent to 1.0 ms.
- The gain shows how many volts each division is worth. In this case each division is worth 2.0 V.
- The period of the wave, T, is the time for one complete cycle. For this AC the period is 4.0 ms.
- You can calculate the frequency of the AC using:

$$T = \frac{1}{f}$$

$$f = \frac{1}{T} = \frac{1}{4.0 \times 10^{-3}} = 250\,\text{Hz}$$

- The peak of this AC is 2.5 squares high. The voltage of this AC is therefore:

$$2.5 \times 2 = 5.0\,\text{V}$$

- You can now calculate the rms voltage using:

$$V_{rms} = \frac{V_{peak}}{\sqrt{2}}$$

$$V_{rms} = \frac{V_{peak}}{\sqrt{2}} = \frac{5.0}{\sqrt{2}} = 3.54\,\text{V}$$

- This AC can therefore be described as a 3.54 V 250 Hz supply.

> ### Exam tip
> Make sure you can convert milliseconds (ms) to seconds.

Do you know?

1 State what is meant by 'AC'.

2 State the relationship between peak current and rms current for an AC supply.

3 The trace from an oscilloscope is shown in Figure 3.5.

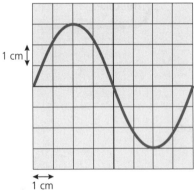

Figure 3.5

The time base setting is 12.5 ms cm⁻¹ and the Y gain setting is 5.0 V cm⁻¹.

  a Determine the peak voltage.

  b Determine the period of the AC.

  c Calculate the rms voltage.

  d Calculate the frequency of the supply.

3.2 Current, p.d., power and resistance

You need to know

- how to carry out calculations involving potential difference, current, power and resistance
- how to use equations with electrical circuits
- how potential dividers work
- how to solve problems involving potential divider circuits

Electrical circuits

This section of the course is different from the others. If you have already studied the National 5 course, then this section should be familiar to you. What is different here is the complexity of the circuits and the contexts you will be expected to understand. It is therefore important that you fully grasp the basics of electricity so you can cope with the exam questions.

Series circuits

The following rules apply to components in a **series circuit**.

- The current is the same at all points in the circuit:

$$I_1 = I_2 = I_3 = \dots = I_n$$

- The potential differences across all the individual components add up to the potential difference of the supply:

$$V_T = V_1 + V_2 + \dots + V_n$$

- The total resistance of the circuit is the sum of the resistances of all the series components:

$$R_T = R_1 + R_2 + \dots + R_n$$

- The total resistance of a series circuit is always higher than the largest resistance in the circuit.

> ### Key term
>
> **Series circuit** A circuit in which all the components are arranged to form a single electrical path.

Parallel circuits

The following rules apply to components in a **parallel circuit**.

- The currents in all the branches add up to the supply current:

$$I_T = I_1 + I_2 + \dots + I_n$$

> ### Key term
>
> **Parallel circuit** A circuit in which the components are arranged in separate branches.

- The potential difference across each component is the same:

$$V_1 = V_2 = V_3 = \ldots = V_n$$

- The total resistance of the components is calculated using:

$$\frac{1}{R_T} = \frac{1}{R_1} + \frac{1}{R_2} + \ldots + \frac{1}{R_n}$$

- The total resistance of components in a parallel circuit is always lower than the smallest individual resistance.

Power

- The **power** of any device, P, is the number of joules of energy it converts every second:

$$P = \frac{E}{t}$$

- Power is measured in watts. One watt is equal to one joule per second.
- In electrical circuits, power can be calculated using the following equations:

$$P = IV = I^2R$$

$$P = \frac{V^2}{R}$$

Potential dividers

- **Potential dividers** are also known as voltage dividers. They consist of two or more resistors (or other components with resistance) connected in series. Figure 3.6 shows an example.

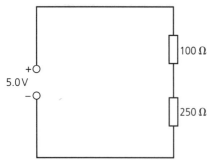

Figure 3.6

- Because the two resistors in this circuit are connected in series, they will have the same current flowing through them.
- This current is equal to the potential difference divided by the resistance:

$$I = \frac{V}{R}$$

■ The current in each resistor is the same, $I_1 = I_2$, therefore:

$$\frac{V_1}{R_1} = \frac{V_2}{R_2}$$

which can be rearranged to give:

$$\frac{V_1}{V_2} = \frac{R_1}{R_2}$$

■ This means that the ratio of the resistances in a potential divider is equal to the ratio of the potential differences across the resistors.
■ Another equation that can be used with potential dividers is:

$$V_1 = \left(\frac{R_1}{R_1 + R_2}\right) V_s$$

where V_s is the supply voltage.
■ Potential dividers can be used to deliver a particular voltage to a device in a circuit.

Mixed circuits

Sometimes you will be presented with more complicated circuits that are a mixture of series and parallel. You will need to solve each individually first. Remember to apply the correct rules for components in series and parallel circuits.

The following are a few examples of the type of thing you can expect.

Example

You could be asked to calculate the total resistance of the circuit shown in Figure 3.7.

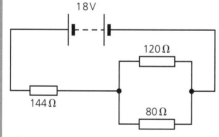

Figure 3.7

First, you need to calculate the total resistance of the two resistors in parallel:

$$\frac{1}{R_T} = \frac{1}{R_1} + \frac{1}{R_2} = \frac{1}{120} + \frac{1}{80} = \frac{2}{240} + \frac{3}{240} = \frac{5}{240}$$

$$R_T = \frac{240}{5} = 48\,\Omega$$

This is the resistance that is equivalent to the two resistors in parallel. In effect, you could replace these two resistors with a single resistor of $48\,\Omega$ and it would not affect the rest of the circuit.

To get the total resistance of the circuit, you now have to add this resistance to the resistor in series with the parallel section:

$$R_T = R_1 + R_2 = 144 + 48 = 192\,\Omega$$

Example

For the circuit in Figure 3.8 you need to follow a different route to arrive at the total resistance.

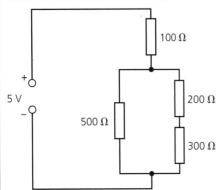

Figure 3.8

First, you need to find the total resistance of the two resistors in series in the right-hand parallel branch:

$$R_T = R_1 + R_2 = 200 + 300 = 500\,\Omega$$

You can now solve the rest of the problem in the same way as the example above:

$$\frac{1}{R_T} = \frac{1}{R_1} + \frac{1}{R_2} = \frac{1}{500} + \frac{1}{500} = \frac{2}{500}$$

$$R_T = \frac{500}{2} = 250\,\Omega$$

$$R_T = R_1 + R_2 = 250 + 100 = 350\,\Omega$$

This is the total resistance of the circuit.

Example

Figure 3.9 shows one final example of how to calculate the total resistance of a circuit.

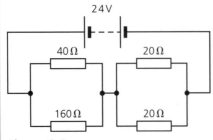

Figure 3.9

You need to find the two total resistances of each of the parallel sections separately.

The left-hand section is determined below:

$$\frac{1}{R_T} = \frac{1}{R_1} + \frac{1}{R_2} = \frac{1}{40} + \frac{1}{160} = \frac{4}{160} + \frac{1}{160} = \frac{5}{160}$$

$$R_T = \frac{160}{5} = 32\,\Omega$$

Next you determine the right-hand section:

$$\frac{1}{R_T} = \frac{1}{R_1} + \frac{1}{R_2} = \frac{1}{20} + \frac{1}{20} = \frac{2}{20}$$

$$R_T = \frac{20}{2} = 10\,\Omega$$

To get the total resistance of the circuit, you now need to add the two total parallel resistances together:

$$R_T = R_1 + R_2 = 32 + 10 = 42\,\Omega$$

The total resistance of the circuit is $42\,\Omega$.

Do you know?

1. State the relationship between the currents in the branches of a parallel circuit and the supply current.

2. A $12\,\Omega$ resistor is connect in series with a $25\,\Omega$ resistor. Calculate the total resistance of this arrangement.

3. A $6.0\,\Omega$ resistor is connected in parallel with a $4.0\,\Omega$ resistor. Calculate the total resistance of this arrangement.

4. What is meant by the term 'power'?

5. A current of $12\,\text{mA}$ flows through a $25\,\Omega$ resistor for $16\,\text{s}$. Determine the maximum amount of heat energy transferred by the resistor.

6. The circuit shown in Figure 3.10 is set up.

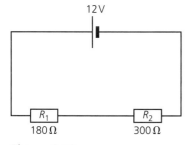

Figure 3.10

Calculate the potential difference across resistor R_1.

3.3 Electrical sources and internal resistance

You need to know

- what is meant by the terms 'electromotive force' (EMF), 'internal resistance', 'lost volts', 'terminal potential difference' (t.p.d.), 'ideal supplies', 'short circuit' and 'open circuit'
- how to use appropriate relationships to solve problems involving EMF, lost volts, t.p.d, current, internal resistance and external resistance
- $E = V + Ir$
- $V = IR$
- how to determine the EMF, internal resistance and short circuit current using graphical analysis

Cells and electrical energy

- When cells are connected in a circuit they supply energy to the main component(s). The amount of energy transferred, the current and the voltage can all be affected by the nature of the cell itself. Different cells have different characteristics and you need to be able to factor these in when determining current and voltage in a particular circuit.

- A cell is composed of metals and acids (or alkalis). When the chemical reaction takes place, charges move and energy is transferred to the rest of the circuit. The charges have to travel through the cell and this acts like a resistor. The cell is said to have an **internal resistance**, r.

- This internal resistance has to be considered when calculating the current, voltage and energy transferred in a circuit. The chemical reaction supplies the charges with energy. If a cell is assumed to have no internal resistance, it is said to be an **ideal cell**. In effect this means we use the quoted voltage of the cell in our calculations, and the cell itself does not have any impact on the external circuit. In reality though the cell does have an effect.

- The amount of energy that the charges 'receive' during the reaction is described as the electromotive force, **EMF**, E. The EMF is the total energy provided by the source to the unit charge flowing through it in joules per coulomb, or more usually called volts.

Key terms

Internal resistance
An indicator of a cell's electrical property that can affect the overall output from that cell.

EMF 'Electromotive force' – the total energy provided by a source to a unit charge flowing through it, measured in volts.

- The charges expend some of the energy to overcome the internal resistance of the cell. They have 'lost' some of the volts from the reaction (EMF), so the potential across the terminals (t.p.d.) is now lower than the EMF.
- The EMF minus the '**lost volts**' equals the t.p.d. This can be represented by:

$$E - Ir = V$$

which can be rearranged to give:

$$E = V + Ir$$

- When a cell is connected in a circuit we have to alter how we symbolise this to acknowledge the internal resistance. The cell is represented as shown in Figure 3.11.

- When a cell is connected in a circuit and is operating, the overall resistance of the circuit is calculated by adding the external resistance of the circuit, R, to the internal resistance of the cell, r.
- A truer representation of what happens in a circuit is shown in Figure 3.12.

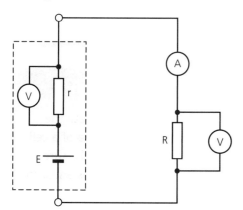

Figure 3.12 The EMF is made up of the potential difference across r and the potential difference across the resistor

- The total resistance is calculated by combining the external and internal resistances. The current in the circuit is calculated using Ohm's law:

$$I = \frac{V}{R}$$

which becomes:

$$I = \frac{E}{(R + r)}$$

and is also given by:

$$\frac{V_{tpd}}{R}$$

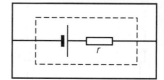

Figure 3.11 A cell has an internal resistance with the symbol r, which is measured in ohms

- Calculating or measuring the EMF and internal resistance of a cell is not straightforward. The following equation has four variables:

$$E = V + Ir$$

which can be rearranged to give:

$$V = -rI + E$$

- This equation is now in the form of $y = mx + c$.
- We can construct a circuit as shown in Figure 3.13, then vary the external resistance, R, and take readings of V and I.

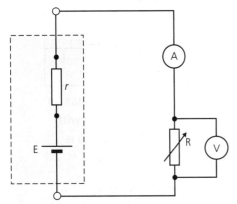

Figure 3.13

- Plotting a graph of V against I gives a straight line with a negative gradient. Calculating the negative of the slope of the line gives the internal resistance, r, and extrapolating the line to the y-axis gives the value for the EMF.
- One point to note is that the EMF value occurs only when no current is drawn from the cell. This agrees with our equation:

$$E = V + Ir$$

When $I = 0$, the term Ir is also zero and therefore $E = V$.

> **Exam tip**
>
> Take care when inserting values into equations. Many simple errors occur when inserting incorrect values for E or V.

> **Exam tip**
>
> When you calculate the internal resistance of a cell from a graph, make sure you state that it is equal to the negative of the slope of the line.

Short circuit current

- The **short circuit current** is the maximum current that a cell can technically produce. It occurs when we connect a lead between the terminals of a battery with no external resistance. This 'short circuits' the cell. With no external resistance, R, the current is given by:

$$I = \frac{E}{r}$$

- It is not advisable to do this because it can drain a cell quickly and cause serious overheating.

> **Key term**
>
> Short circuit current
> The current generated by a cell when a conductor is connected across its terminals.

- For example, a standard 1.5 V (EMF) cell with an internal resistance of $0.8\,\Omega$ will give a short circuit current of:

$$I = \frac{1.5}{0.8} = 1.9\,A$$

- A lead-acid car battery of EMF 12 V can have an internal resistance of $0.05\,\Omega$. This gives a short circuit current of:

$$I = \frac{12}{0.05} = 240\,A$$

- This value is extremely high and if jump leads were to connect across this there would be sparks, large amounts of heat and the battery could break up and spray acid into the air.

- Graphically, a short circuit current can be worked out by extrapolating the line of a V against I graph to the x-axis. This gives the maximum current possible, which also occurs when there is no terminal potential difference. The lost volts are equal to the EMF and therefore no voltage is available for external use.

Do you know?

1 A cell with an EMF of 1.50 V and an internal resistance of $1.80\,\Omega$ is connected to a resistor of $12.0\,\Omega$. Calculate:

   a the current in the circuit

   b the voltage across the resistor

   c the lost volts

2 A car battery of EMF 12.5 V can produce a short circuit current of 165 A. Calculate its internal resistance.

3 A resistor of $25\,\Omega$ in a circuit has a current of 0.45 A through it. The cell has an internal resistance of $1.8\,\Omega$. Calculate the EMF and the lost volts.

4 A student obtains the following results for the voltage across and the current through a resistor. He used a cell connected to a variable resistor.

Table 3.1

p.d. across resistor/V	Current through resistor/A
4.0	0.41
3.0	0.88
2.0	1.40
1.0	1.95

Use these results to plot a graph and then determine the EMF and the internal resistance of the cell.

3.4 Capacitors

You need to know

- a capacitor of 1 farad will store 1 coulomb of charge when the potential difference is 1 volt
- the energy stored in a charged capacitor is equal to the area under a charge–potential difference graph
- how to use appropriate relationships to solve problems involving energy, charge, capacitance and potential difference
- how current and voltage vary with time for both a charging and a discharging capacitor
- the effect of varying the resistance on the charging and discharging of a capacitor

Capacitance

- **Capacitors** are common components in many electrical and electronic circuits. They are used to store charge and energy. They were developed hundreds of years ago and nowadays can be small components that are used widely.
- When a capacitor is connected in a simple circuit, such as the one shown in Figure 3.14, charge flows to the capacitor and this in turn creates a potential difference across the capacitor.

Key terms

Capacitor A device for storing charge and energy.

Capacitance The amount of charge stored per volt.

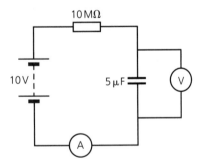

Figure 3.14

- When more charge is supplied to the capacitor, it causes a higher voltage across the capacitor. The ratio of charge to voltage is referred to as **capacitance** and is measured in farads:

$$\text{capacitance} = \frac{\text{charge}}{\text{voltage}}$$

$$C = \frac{Q}{V}$$

- When one coulomb (1 C) of charge is transferred this causes a potential difference of one volt (1 V) across the capacitor and the capacitor then has a capacitance of 1 F.
- 1 F is considered to be a large capacitance and you are more likely to come across capacitances of millifarads (10^{-3} F, mF) or microfarads (10^{-6} F, µF).
- A large capacitor requires a large amount of charge (1 C) to reach 1 V. A small capacitor requires a smaller amount of charge to reach 1 V.
- Physically, capacitors cannot be charged to higher and higher voltages. Most capacitors have a limit on their side and they must not exceed this voltage. A limit of 25 V, for example, tells us that the capacitor will work safely at voltages beneath this value. If this voltage is exceeded, the capacitor will break down and the heat generated could lead to a build-up of pressure and possible explosion.
- When a capacitor is charging, the voltage across its terminals increases. This reduces the current transferring charge to the capacitor, because the potential difference between the supply and the capacitor decreases. This makes it difficult to measure or determine the charge stored on a capacitor because the current is continually changing.
- If we could charge a capacitor using a constant-charging current we could calculate the amount of charge transferred to the capacitor using:

charge = current × time

$Q = It$

Energy stored in a capacitor

- A capacitor can be charged by connecting it to an electrical supply in a simple series circuit. As more charge is stored by the capacitor, the potential difference across the capacitor increases in direct proportion, as shown in Figure 3.15.

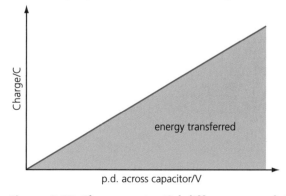

energy transferred

Charge/C

p.d. across capacitor/V

Figure 3.15 Charge–potential difference graph for a capacitor

- The energy stored in the capacitor can be calculated from the area under the charge–potential difference graph. This area is a triangle, so you use the formula for the area of a triangle, in this case:

$$E = \frac{1}{2}QV$$

- The capacitance can be calculated using:

$$C = \frac{Q}{V}$$

which can be rearranged to give:

$$Q = \frac{C}{V}$$

and:

$$V = \frac{Q}{C}$$

- These relationships can be combined with the area under the graph equation to give:

$$E = \frac{1}{2}QV$$

and

$$E = \frac{1}{2}CV^2$$

Charging a capacitor

- When a capacitor is connected in a circuit as shown in Figure 3.16, it will charge until it reaches the same potential difference across it as the supply that is charging it. When it reaches this, there is no potential difference between the supply and the capacitor, and therefore no charging current. The capacitor is said to be 'fully charged'.

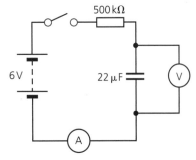

Figure 3.16

- The graphs of voltage and current against time for a charging capacitor are shown in Figure 3.17.

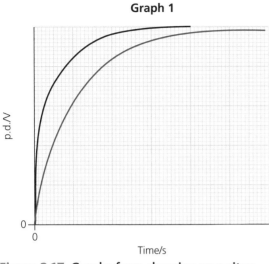
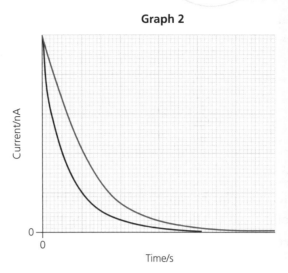

Figure 3.17 Graphs for a charging capacitor

- In Graph 1, as charge is transferred to the capacitor the p.d. across the capacitor increases until it reaches the same potential as the supply. At this point, no current flows and no more charge is transferred to the capacitor.
- In Graph 2, the capacitor has no charge initially and therefore no p.d. As current flows and charge is transferred the p.d. of the capacitor increases and as a result the p.d. between the capacitor and supply reduces. This reduces the current flowing (due to Ohm's law). When the potential of the capacitor reaches the same potential as the supply, there is no potential difference and therefore no current.
- On both graphs, the black lines show sample curves for a capacitor with a smaller capacitance. It requires less charge to reach the same voltage and as a result it charges and discharges more quickly.
- The size of the current flowing in a circuit is determined by the potential difference and also by the resistance of the circuit. If we were to increase the resistance of the circuit to $1\,M\Omega$, the time taken for the capacitors to charge and discharge would increase. The final p.d. across the capacitor would *not* be affected by the change in resistance.
- Resistance only has an effect on the current, not on the supply voltage or the final voltage across the capacitor. An increase in resistance increases the time taken to charge. It does *not* affect the final voltage, the energy or the charge transferred.

Discharging a capacitor

- The circuit shown in Figure 3.18 can be used to examine what happens to the voltage across a capacitor, and the current to and from a capacitor, when it is discharging.

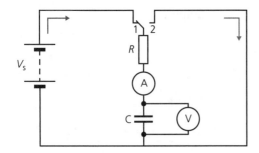

Figure 3.18

- In this example, the capacitor is charged by connecting the switch to Point 1 and it is discharged by turning the switch to Point 2.
- When the current from the supply flows to the capacitor, it charges the capacitor. When the switch is moved to Point 2 the capacitor discharges through the right-hand circuit. This means the current is in the opposite direction to the charging current, because the 'side' of the capacitor that gained electrons now loses electrons.
- Because the capacitor charges and discharges through the same resistor, R, the times taken for it to charge and discharge should be the same. This gives a graph of p.d. against time for a charging and discharging capacitor similar to the one shown in Figure 3.19.

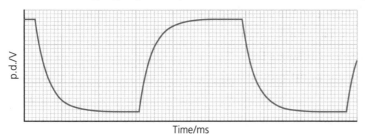

Figure 3.19 Graph for a discharging capacitor

Current–discharge graphs

- Based on the set up in Figure 3.16, in the first section of the graph the current is initially at its maximum value, as shown in Figure 3.20. This can be calculated using:

$$\frac{V_s}{R}$$

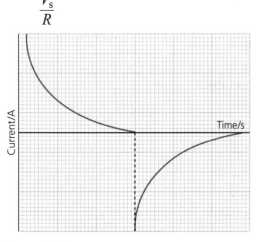

Figure 3.20

- As the capacitor starts to charge, the potential difference between the supply and the capacitor decreases and so does the current. When the capacitor is at the same p.d. as the supply, no current flows.
- When the switch is moved to Point 2 the capacitor discharges through the resistor around the right-hand circuit. The initial current is given by:

$$I = \frac{V}{R}$$

- This current is in the opposite direction to the charging current, therefore it is negative with respect to the charging current's direction.
- If we were to continually turn the switch to Point 1, then Point 2, then Point 1 and so on, the graph would be a continuation of Figure 3.20, repeated again and again.

> ### Exam tip
>
> Make sure you learn the shapes of the graphs for current and voltage against time for charging and discharging a capacitor.

Examples

1 A 220 μF capacitor is attached to 9 V cell. Calculate the charge stored on the capacitor.

$Q = CV = 220 \times 10^{-6} \times 9 = 1.98 \times 10^{-3}$ C

2 A 450 mF capacitor is charged through a 275 Ω resistor by a 12.0 V supply.

a Calculate the initial charging current.

$$I = \frac{V}{R} = \frac{12}{275} = 0.044 \text{ A}$$

b What is the final p.d. across the capacitor when it is fully charged?

12 V

c Calculate the energy stored in the capacitor when it is fully charged.

$E = \frac{1}{2}CV^2 = \frac{1}{2} \times 450 \times 10^{-3} \times 12^2 = 32.4$ J

Do you know?

1 A 47 mF capacitor is charged from a 12 V supply, as shown in Figure 3.21. It is charged via the 200 kΩ resistor and discharged through the 500 kΩ resistor.

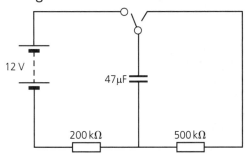

Figure 3.21

a Calculate the charge stored on the capacitor.

b Calculate the energy stored in the capacitor.

c Calculate the initial charging current.

d Calculate the initial discharging current.

2 A student sets up a circuit to charge a capacitor with a 9 V supply and a 25 000 Ω resistor. The capacitor charges up in 15 s. (Exact values are not required for your answers, but indicative values should be provided.)

a Sketch graphs of the voltage across the capacitor, and the current during charging.

b The capacitor discharges through a 15 000 Ω resistor. Sketch the graph of the current discharging against time.

3 A 2200 μF capacitor is charged using a 16 V supply in a circuit with a 15 000 Ω resistor. The 15 000 Ω resistor is then replaced by a 10 000 Ω resistor and the capacitor is charged again. What difference would changing to this new resistor make to:

a the final charge on the capacitor

b the final voltage across the capacitor

c the initial charging current

d the energy stored in the capacitor?

3.5 Semiconductors and p–n junctions

You need to know

- what is meant by the terms 'conduction band' and 'valence band'
- solids can be categorised as insulators, conductors or semiconductors
- in order for a solid to conduct there must be free electrons and accessible empty states
- how to describe the electrical properties of solids using band theory
- how to describe the effect of changing temperature on semiconductor properties
- how doping can produce n-type and p-type semiconductors
- there is an electric field in a p–n junction
- how to describe the movement of electrons in a p–n junction
- what is meant by the terms 'forward bias' and 'reverse bias'
- how to describe the production of photons in an LED
- how to describe the operation of a solar cell

Semiconductors

- There are materials that can conduct under certain conditions and you need to know how to explain their properties in terms of **conduction bands** and **valence bands**.

- Atoms have energy levels and these are filled with electrons. They are filled, in order, outwards from the nucleus.

- Bands are formed when atoms come together to form a solid or other compound. The energy levels of an atom combine with other energy levels to form **bands**. Bands are more of a *group* property, whereas levels are a singular, atomic property.

- Electrons in the outermost levels are called the valence electrons and these are the most easily removed. These valence electrons are found in the **valence band** of solids.

- The energy bands are formed around the nucleus in a similar fashion to energy levels. The bands are separated from each other and the separation between the bands is referred to as energy gaps or **band gaps**.

- The gaps between the bands are used to explain certain semiconductor phenomena.

- The bands are filled with electrons from the atoms. The highest filled band is the valence band, which contains valence electrons.

- The first unfilled band is called the **conduction band** and this is where electrical conduction occurs.

- The gap between the valence band and the conduction band is referred to as the 'band gap'.

- The size of the band gap determines whether the material is an insulator or a semiconductor. Figure 3.22 shows that:
  - ☐ **Insulators:** have a large gap between the conduction and valence bands. Electrons cannot move from the valence band to the conduction band.
  - ☐ **Semiconductors:** have a small gap between the bands. Under certain conditions electrons can gain enough energy to overcome the gap.
  - ☐ **Conductors:** there is no gap between the conduction and valence bands. Metals do not have a band gap. There are free electrons and therefore the material is conductive.

Key terms

Conduction band The first unfilled band above the valence band in a solid.

Valence band The highest occupied band in a solid.

Synoptic link

The Bohr model of the atom describes the structure of atoms. See page 58.

Key terms

Insulator A solid in which the valence band is full.

Semiconductor A solid in which the gap between the valence band and the conduction band is small.

Conductor A solid in which the conduction band and valence band overlap, or the valence band is only partially filled.

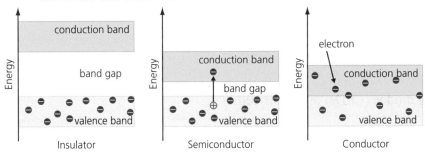

Figure 3.22

Doping

- Elements in Group IV of the periodic table can be 'doped'. This means that atoms from Groups III or VI elements can be added to silicon, for example, to affect its conducting properties.
- In **doping**, when a Group V element is added, this adds an extra electron which goes to the conduction band. This creates an **n-type semiconductor**.
- When a Group III element is added, there is a 'missing' electron and this draws an electron from the valence band creating a 'hole'. This creates a **p-type semiconductor**.

> **Key term**
>
> **Doping** The process by which impurities are added to a semiconductor in order to increase its conductivity.

p–n junctions

Many semiconductor devices combine p- and n-type materials to form a **p–n junction**, as shown in Figure 3.23.

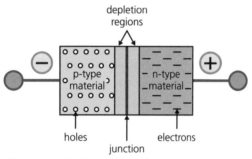

Figure 3.23 A p–n junction

> **Key term**
>
> **p–n junction** Made by placing a p-type material and an n-type material in contact with each other.

The junction has some key characteristics.

- The region around the junction is stripped of the free electrons and holes, and this leaves behind charged ions.
- The depletion region that is formed has an electric field.
- This field can act as barrier to block the flow of current.

When a voltage is applied to the junction it can do one of two things.

1 When the voltage is applied in the 'forward' direction, this reduces the electric field blocking the flow of current and the junction can then allow current to flow. This is described as **forward bias**.

2 When the voltage is applied in the opposite (or reverse) direction, this increases the electric field and no current will flow. This is described as **reverse bias**.

There are several semiconductor devices that rely on the characteristics of p–n junctions that are critical to modern technology, such as light-emitting diodes (LEDs) and solar cells.

Light-emitting diodes (LEDs)

- An LED is forward biased p–n junction that emits photons. It will 'light up' when a potential difference is applied to it in forward bias.
- Electrons move from the conduction band of the n-type semiconductor to the conduction band of the p-type semiconductor. Photons are emitted when electrons 'drop' from the conduction band into the valence band either side of the junction.

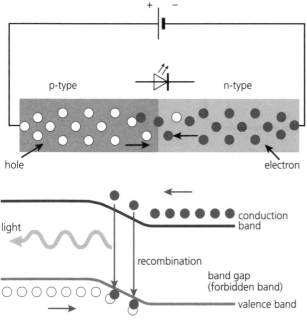

Figure 3.24 Energy bands in an LED: the energy released as the electron drops from the conduction band to the valence band is emitted as light energy

> ### Exam tip
>
> Make sure you can describe how an LED works in terms of the movement of electrons in the bands of the semiconductor material.

> ### Synoptic link
>
> For a description of photons inside an atom see page 51.

Solar cells

- A solar cell is a semiconductor device that generates a potential difference when photons are incident on it. This is known as the **photovoltaic effect**.
- The absorption of the photons allows electrons to 'rise' from the valence band to the conduction band. The p–n junction causes the electrons in the conduction band to move towards the n-type semiconductor and this movement produces a potential difference across the solar cell.

Do you know?

1 State whether each of these statements is true or false:

   a   In insulators the gap between the valence band and conduction band is small.

   b   In conductors the conduction band is filled with electrons.

   c   Increasing the temperature of a semiconductor increases its conductivity.

   d   In metals the highest occupied energy band is not completely full.

   e   The gap between the valence band and conduction band is larger in semiconductors than in insulators.

2 Explain how an LED operates.

3 Describe the relative positions of the conduction band and valence band for:

   a   a conductor

   b   an insulator

End of section 3 questions

1   A DC current of 0.25 A flows through a 24 Ω resistor.

   a   Calculate the potential difference across the resistor.

   b   Determine the number of joules of electrical energy transferred to heat in the resistor in 1 minute.

   The DC supply is replaced by an AC supply. The resistor converts the same number of joules of electrical energy as it did before.

   c   Determine the peak current of the AC supply.

2   A packet contains two 12 Ω resistors and two 24 Ω resistors.

   a   Determine the maximum resistance that can be obtained using all four resistors.

   b   Determine the minimum resistance that can be obtained using all four resistors.

   c   How can the four resistors be arranged to produce a total resistance of 18 Ω?

3   A battery of EMF 6.00 V and internal resistance 1.20 Ω is connected to 3.80 Ω load resistor.

   a   Determine:

      i   the lost volts in the battery

      ii   the t.p.d. of the battery

      iii   the power dissipated in the resistor

   A second 3.8 Ω resistor is connected in parallel with the original load resistor.

   b   Does the t.p.d. increase, decrease or stay the same?

      Justify your answer.

4 A 220 μF capacitor is charged using a 2.4 V power supply.

   a Determine the maximum charge stored on the capacitor.

   b Determine the maximum energy stored in the capacitor.

   The fully-charged capacitor is removed from the power source. It is now connected to a lamp that has a resistance of 3.0 Ω.

   c Determine the initial current in the bulb.

   d State what happens to the size of the current in the bulb as the capacitor discharges.

5 In a scientific experiment a capacitor is charged using a 230 V supply. It is connected in series with a 7.5 kΩ resistor. The capacitor has a value of 775 μF.

   a Calculate the initial charging current.

   b Sketch a graph of how the voltage across the capacitor varies with time from the moment the capacitor is connected to the supply.

   c Calculate the energy stored in the capacitor.

   d The same capacitor is discharged through an electrical component in a time of 250 μs. Calculate the average power output of the component during this phase.

6 Describe what 'doping' means and how we create a p-type semiconductor and an n-type semiconductor.

7 Explain the difference between conductors and insulators in terms of bands.

8 A capacitor is charged using a 12 V battery in series with a 2.5 kΩ resistor. At one point during the charging the capacitor stores 65 mC of charge and is at a voltage of 9.5 V.

   a Calculate the capacitance of the capacitor.

   b Calculate the energy stored in the capacitor when it is fully charged.

   c Calculate the charge stored on the capacitor when fully charged.

   d Calculate the initial charging current.

4 The assignment

You need to know

- you need to be able to write up an assignment
- you should do approximately 8 hours research for your assignment
- you must do at least one experiment
- your write up must be completed in 2 hours
- your completed assignment will be submitted to SQA for marking

Research phase

- You should agree your area of research with your teacher or lecturer.
- They can also advise you on the aim of your assignment, but you should write your own aim in your own words.
- One component of your research is that you must take part in an experiment. There can be a maximum of four people in a group for this part of the assignment.
- Your teacher or lecturer can supply you with experimental instructions, but you must take part in the experiment yourself.

Report phase

You are allowed to take the following items with you into the report phase of your assignment:

- SQA's instructions for candidates
- the raw data from your experiment
- data from an internet or literature source
- information required to reference a source
- an experimental instruction sheet

You are not allowed to take:

- a draft of your report
- a draft of the background physics
- any processed data
- any specimen calculations

Exam tip

Avoid using the word 'if' in your aim. It can lead to a trivial conclusion that will lose you marks in the write up.

Exam tip

Make sure your experiment allows you to draw a scatter graph. This is the only type of graph that can gain marks in the assignment.

Exam tip

Make sure you refer to the candidate instructions as you write up your report.

- a graph of your results
- a draft of your analysis, conclusion or evaluation

Aim

Make sure your aim is clear.

Underlying physics

Your underlying physics should refer to your aim. Keep this brief because you only have 2 hours to complete the entire write up.

Data handling and collection

- You need to summarise your experimental method. This must be in your own words and include details of how the measurements were made. This again should be brief. A diagram is a good idea but will not be enough on its own.
- You must have repeated measurements of your data.
- Your data should be in table format with the correct headings and units.
- You must include data from a second experiment, or from a literature or internet source, that relates to your aim.
- If you are including data from a second experiment, you must give a citation and a reference for your background physics.
- If you are including data from a second source, you must give a citation and a reference.

> **Exam tip**
>
> Make sure you give the date for internet references.

Graphical presentation

- You must plot a scatter graph.
- You must plot your own data.
- Your graph must have suitable scales with correct units and labels. If possible, you should draw a line of best fit.

> **Exam tip**
>
> If you generate a graph using a spreadsheet, it must have major and minor grid lines and the points must not be too large.

Uncertainties

- You should have reading uncertainties in all your measurements.
- You should have random uncertainties in all your repeated measurements.

> **Exam tip**
>
> Make sure the line you draw covers the entire range of your data.

Analysis

Your analysis should be a consideration of your data. This could include calculating a constant – for example, using the gradient of your line, or the absolute uncertainty in a final value.

Conclusion

Your conclusion must refer to all your data.

Evaluation

- You get 1 mark for each correct evaluative statement you make.
- Only 1 mark is available for the evaluation of data from an internet source.
- 2 marks come from your experiment.
- Any evaluative statements must be supported by an explanation. For example, if you have large random uncertainties, you could say 'repeating the experiment more times would be an improvement because it would reduce my random uncertainties'.

Structure

- Your assignment should have a structure that is easy to follow.
- This includes having an informative title. Titles such as 'Physics assignment' or 'Batteries' are not informative, whereas something like 'The internal resistance of a battery' is.